D1404633

Complete
Canadian
Curriculum

MATH
ENGLISH
SOCIAL STUDIES
SCIENCE

Grade **3**

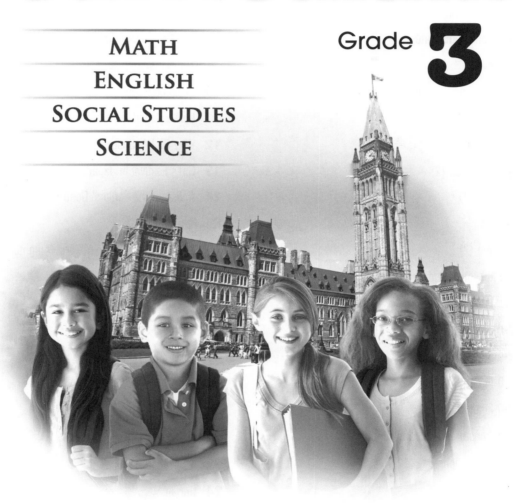

ISBN: 978-1-897164-31-0

Contents Grade 3

Mathematics

English

ISBN: 978-1-897164-31-0

Social Studies

Science

ISBN: 978-1-897164-31-0

ISBN: 978-1-897164-31-0

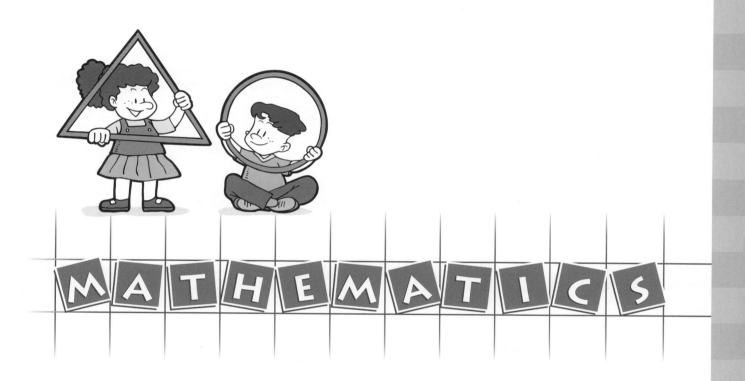

MATHEMATICS

ISBN: 978-1-897164-31-0

Numbers to 100

- Compare, order, and write in words whole numbers to 100.
- Count backwards by 2's, 5's, and 10's from 100.
- Round 2-digit numbers to the nearest ten.

10 beads in a group

I have thirty-two beads.

Fill in the missing numbers.

① 35 36 _____ 38 _____ _____ _____ 42 _____

② 69 70 _____ _____ 73 _____ _____ _____ 77

③ 87 88 _____ _____ _____ 92 93 _____ _____

④ 55 56 _____ 58 _____ _____ _____ _____ 63

Circle the greater number.

⑤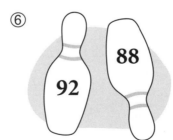
36 49

⑥
92 88

⑦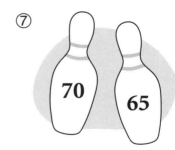
70 65

Put the numbers in order from least to greatest.

⑧ 39 58 63 18 _____

⑨ 44 30 81 53 _____

⑩ 64 16 46 14 _____

6

ISBN: 978-1-897164-31-0

Count and write the numbers in words.

⑪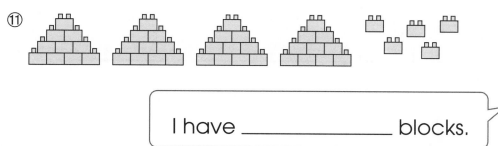

I have _____ blocks.

⑫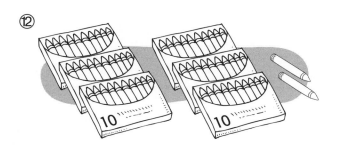

_____ crayons

⑬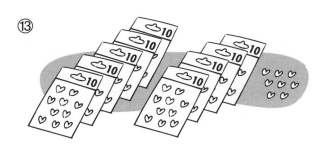

_____ stickers

Write the numbers.

⑭ twenty-six   _____   ⑮ forty-five   _____

⑯ ninety-one   _____   ⑰ eighty   _____

⑱ sixty-four   _____   ⑲ thirty-eight   _____

⑳ seventy-two   _____   ㉑ fifty-three   _____

㉒ a number greater than 65   _____

㉓ a number greater than 28, but smaller than 37   _____

㉔ a 2-digit number with 0 in its ones column   _____

㉕ a 2-digit number with 4 in its tens column   _____

ISBN: 978-1-897164-31-0

Follow the patterns to write numbers and draw arrows on the number lines.

㉖

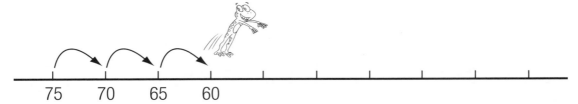

75 70 65 60

㉗

100 90 80 70

㉘

88 86 84 82

Count backwards by 2's, 5's, or 10's to find the missing numbers. Write the numbers.

㉙ 74 _____ 70 68 _____ _____ 62 _____ _____ 56

㉚ 90 85 _____ _____ 70 _____ _____ _____ 50 45

㉛ 100 _____ _____ 70 60 _____ _____ 30 _____ 10

Put the numbers in order from greatest to least. Then fill in the blanks.

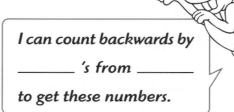

㉜ 32 30 34 28

In order: _____

I can count backwards by _____ 's from _____ to get these numbers.

I can count backwards by _____ 's from _____ to get these numbers.

㉝ 45 60 50 55

In order: _____

ISBN: 978-1-897164-31-0

Rounding a 2-digit number to the nearest ten:

e.g. 46 ⟵ It is between 40 and 50.

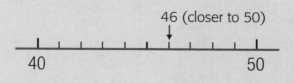

46 (closer to 50)

40   50

46 is rounded to __50__ .

> *A number halfway between 2 numbers should be rounded up. For example, 35 is rounded to 40.*

Use an arrow to locate each number on the number line. Then round the number to the nearest ten.

㉞

53

50   60

53 is rounded to _____ .

㉟

88

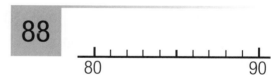

80   90

88 is rounded to _____ .

㊱

69

60   70

69 is rounded to _____ .

㊲

17

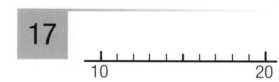

10   20

17 is rounded to _____ .

Fill in the blanks.

㊳

about 80

> *The number of candies in the bottle should be between 75 and _____ .*

㊴

> *The number of beads in the box should be between _____ and _____ .*

Beads
about 50

 ISBN: 978-1-897164-31-0

Addition and Subtraction of 2-Digit Numbers

- Add or subtract 2-digit numbers.
- Estimate or check the answers.
- Solve word problems.

They cost 70¢ only.

```
    1
  3 5
+ 3 5
-----
  7 0
```

35¢ each   35¢ each

Do the addition.

①
```
  3 7
+ 1 6
```

②
```
  4 2
+ 3 9
```

③
```
  1 8
+ 6 3
```

④ 45 + 48 = _____

⑤ 27 + 60 = _____

⑥ 34 + 19 = _____

⑦ 42 + 38 = _____

Round each number to the nearest ten. Do the estimate. Then find the exact answer.

⑧
```
  4 6
+ 3 3
```
Estimate

_____ + _____

⑨
```
  2 4
+ 5 8
```
Estimate

⑩
```
  1 2
+ 5 6
```
Estimate

⑪
```
    9
+ 2 9
```
Estimate

ISBN: 978-1-897164-31-0

The answer to each question is the number of cookies in each cookie jar. Do the subtraction. Then answer the questions.

⑫

A
```
  7 8
- 2 6
```

B
```
  4 0
- 1 7
```

C
```
  5 2
- 3 9
```

D
```
  8 1
- 6 3
```

E
```
  4 3
-   8
```

F
```
  3 5
-   7
```

G 74 – 37 = _____

H 55 – 49 = _____

I 60 – 35 = _____

J 93 – 75 = _____

⑬ Which jars have the same number of cookies? _____

⑭ Which jar has the most cookies? _____

⑮ Which jar has 10 more cookies than C? _____

Round each number to the nearest ten. Do the estimate. Then find the exact answer.

⑯ _____ Estimate
```
  7 4
- 3 9
```

⑰ _____ Estimate
```
  6 8
- 4 1
```

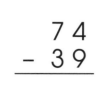

ISBN: 978-1-897164-31-0

Use addition to check the answer of subtraction.

e.g. Is 46 − 27 = __29__ correct?

1st Add the shaded numbers.

```
    4 6
-   2 7
    2 9
```

2nd If the answer is 46, "29" is the correct answer.

```
    1
    2 9
+   2 7
    5 6  ← not 46
```

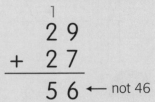

3 16

```
  4̸ 6̸
- 2 7
  1 9
```

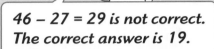

46 − 27 = 29 is not correct.
The correct answer is 19.

Check the answer to each question. Put a check mark ✔ in the space provided if the answer is correct; otherwise, put a cross ✘ and find the correct answer.

⑱ —————————————————— *Check*

```
    7 3          2 4
-   2 4        + 5 9
    5 9  (   )
```

⑲ —————————————————— *Check*

```
    6 0
-   4 5
    1 5  (   )
```

Do the subtraction. Then check the answers.

⑳
```
    9 0
-   1 6
```
Check
```
    +_____
```

㉑
```
    5 9
-   2 4
```
Check

㉒
```
    3 3
-   1 6
```
Check

㉓
```
    8 4
-   6 6
```
Check

ISBN: 978-1-897164-31-0

Solve the problems.

㉔

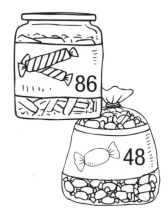

a. How many candies are there in 2 bags?

_____ = _____

_____ candies

b. How many more candies are there in a can than in a bag?

_____ = _____

_____ more

㉕

Tim's cards

36

42

a. How many fewer baseball cards than hockey cards does Tim have?

_____ = _____

_____ fewer

b. How many cards does Tim have in all?

_____ = _____

_____ cards

㉖

62¢

a. A tin soldier costs 5¢ less than a matchbox car. How much does a matchbox car cost?

_____ = _____

_____ ¢

b. *I pay 75¢ for a tin soldier. What is my change?*

_____ = _____

_____ ¢

ISBN: 978-1-897164-31-0

I've packed 556 dolls already.

Numbers to 1000

- Write, compare, and order whole numbers to 1000.
- Identify and represent the value of a digit in a 3-digit number.
- Count by 2's, 5's, 10's, 25's, or 100's.

Count and write the numbers.

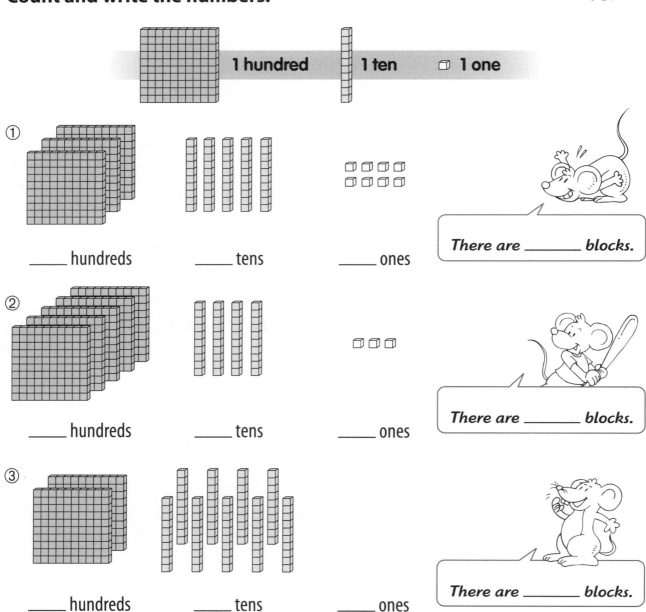

1 hundred **1 ten** **1 one**

① _____ hundreds _____ tens _____ ones

There are _____ blocks.

② _____ hundreds _____ tens _____ ones

There are _____ blocks.

③ _____ hundreds _____ tens _____ ones

There are _____ blocks.

ISBN: 978-1-897164-31-0

Write the numbers. Then answer the questions.

④ **A** _____ = 6 hundreds 5 tens 7 ones

B _____ = 5 hundreds 2 tens 4 ones

C _____ = 9 hundreds 7 tens 6 ones

D 375 = ___ hundreds ___ tens ___ ones

E 581 = _____

⑤ *Which numbers are between 400 and 600?*

_____

⑥ *Which numbers have 5 in its hundreds column?*

_____

Put the numbers in order from greatest to least.

⑦ 652 256 625 _____

⑧ 788 887 878 _____

⑨ 490 940 904 _____

Write the numbers that the arrows are pointing at.

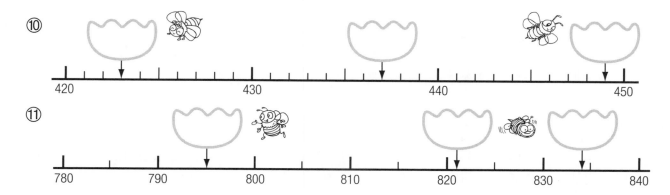

See how many apples were sold in the past three days. Write the numbers. Then answer the questions.

⑫

_____ apples   _____ apples   _____ apples

⑬ On which day were the most apples sold?   _____

⑭ If 4 more apples will be sold on Thursday than on Wednesday, how many apples will be sold on Thursday?   _____ apples

⑮ If 3 fewer apples will be sold on Friday than on Tuesday, how many apples will be sold on Friday?   _____ apples

Follow the patterns to draw arrows and write numbers. Then fill in the blanks to tell how to skip count.

⑯

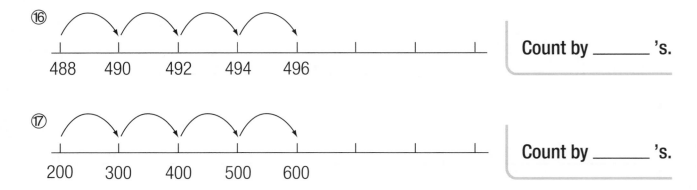

488   490   492   494   496   Count by _____ 's.

⑰

200   300   400   500   600   Count by _____ 's.

          ISBN: 978-1-897164-31-0

Tell how to skip count in each group. Then write the next 5 numbers.

⑱ 425, 450, 475, 500, 525

Count by _____'s: _____

⑲ 700, 710, 720, 730, 740

Count by _____'s: _____

⑳ 690, 695, 700, 705, 710

Count by _____'s: _____

Answer the questions.

㉑  What are the greatest and the least 3-digit numbers?

_____ ; _____

㉒  What are the next five numbers after 398?

_____

㉓ Write 5 numbers that are greater than 388 but smaller than 436.

_____

㉔ How many 3-digit numbers can be formed with these balls? What are they?

_____

_____

ISBN: 978-1-897164-31-0

4

Addition and Subtraction of 3-Digit Numbers (1)

- Add 3-digit numbers with or without grouping.
- Subtract 3-digit numbers with or without borrowing.

No. of Audience:

```
   1 1
     8 9   Adult
 + 1 2 5   Children
 ─────────
   2 1 4   in all
```

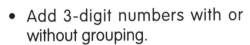

I welcome all 214 of you tonight.

Do the addition.

①
```
   2 3 4
 + 1 0 5
```

②
```
   2 1 6
 + 4 8 3
```

③
```
   4 1 1
 +   8 4
```

④
```
   6 5 3
 + 1 1 4
```

⑤
```
   5 2 1
 +   4 7
```

⑥
```
     6 5
 + 1 0 3
```

⑦ 712 + 124 = _____

⑧ 335 + 161 = _____

⑨ 188 + 210 = _____

⑩ 427 + 402 = _____

Find the answers. Then match the socks with the correct drawers. Write the letters.

⑪

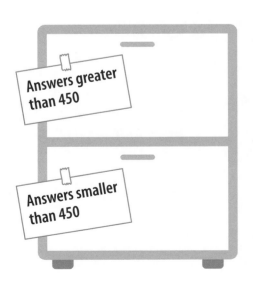

A 224 + 224 = _____

B 205 + 183 = _____

C 73 + 315 = _____

D 157 + 340 = _____

Answers greater than 450

Answers smaller than 450

ISBN: 978-1-897164-31-0

Do the addition.

⑫
```
    ○
  3 2 7
+ 4 5 9
```

⑬
```
    ○
  4 3 6
+ 1 2 7
```

⑭
```
   ○ ○
     8 5
+ 5 1 6
```

⑮
```
  ○ ○
  6 5 2
+ 1 4 9
```

⑯
```
  ○ ○
  5 8 4
+ 2 6 6
```

⑰
```
  ○ ○
  2 9 8
+ 2 9 8
```

⑱ 381 + 65 = _____

⑲ 289 + 350 = _____

⑳ 743 + 79 = _____

㉑ 157 + 644 = _____

㉒ 329 + 165 = _____

㉓ 590 + 286 = _____

Find the answers. Match the toys with the boxes that have the same answers. Write the letters.

㉔ Ⓐ 363 + 174 = _____

Ⓑ 92 + 139 = _____

Ⓒ 402 + 88 = _____

Ⓓ 246 + 309 = _____

Ⓔ 465 + 137 = _____

Ⓕ 203 + 48 = _____

Ⓖ 159 + 159 = _____

ISBN: 978-1-897164-31-0

Steps to do subtraction:

1st Subtract the ones. If the ones are too small, borrow from the tens.

2nd Subtract the tens. If the tens are too small, borrow from the hundreds.

3rd Subtract the hundreds.

$$\begin{array}{r} {}^{6}\cancel{7}\ {}^{10}\cancel{1}\ {}^{15}\cancel{5} \\ -\ 2\ 4\ 8 \\ \hline 4\ 6\ 7 \end{array}$$

$15 - 8 = 7$
$10 - 4 = 6$
$6 - 2 = 4$

$715 - 248 = \underline{\textbf{467}}$

Do the subtraction.

㉕
$$\begin{array}{r} 4\ 7\ 5 \\ -\ 2\ 3\ 4 \\ \hline \end{array}$$

㉖
$$\begin{array}{r} 5\ 2\ 9 \\ -\ 1\ 0\ 8 \\ \hline \end{array}$$

㉗
$$\begin{array}{r} 6\ 8\ 3 \\ -\ 4\ 7\ 2 \\ \hline \end{array}$$

㉘
$$\begin{array}{r} {}^{3}5\ {}^{13}\cancel{4}\cancel{3} \\ -\ 2\ 3\ 4 \\ \hline \end{array}$$

㉙
$$\begin{array}{r} {}^{6}\cancel{7}\ {}^{12}\cancel{3}\ {}^{12}\cancel{2} \\ -\ 4\ 5\ 8 \\ \hline \end{array}$$

㉚
$$\begin{array}{r} {}^{3}\cancel{4}\ {}^{9}\cancel{0}\ {}^{15}\cancel{5} \\ -\quad\ 6\ 7 \\ \hline \end{array}$$

㉛ 354 – 179 = _____

㉜ 602 – 381 = _____

㉝ 710 – 563 = _____

㉞ 934 – 685 = _____

Find the answers. Then put the necklaces in order from the one with the greatest number to the one with the least.

㉟ **A** 539 – 142 = _____

B 700 – 464 = _____

C 351 – 209 = _____

D 802 – 381 = _____

In order: _____

 ISBN: 978-1-897164-31-0

Solve the problems.

㊱ Tim has 245 marbles and George has 173 marbles.

a. How many marbles do the boys have in all?

b. How many more marbles does Tim have than George?

_____ marbles

_____ more

㊲ Lucy has 318 stickers. Katie has 57 fewer stickers than Lucy.

a. How many stickers does Katie have?

b. How many stickers do the girls have in all?

_____ stickers

_____ stickers

㊳ Look at Mrs. Cowan's gifts.

a. What is the price difference between the gifts?

$ _____

b. What is the total cost of the gifts?

$ _____

ISBN: 978-1-897164-31-0

Addition and Subtraction of 3-Digit Numbers (2)

- Add or subtract 3-digit numbers.
- Check and estimate answers.
- Understand the relationship between addition and subtraction.
- Solve word problems.

No. of Cheese Cubes:

$$
\begin{array}{r}
1\ 1 \\
3\ 2\ 6 \\
+\ 2\ 8\ 9 \\
\hline
6\ 1\ 5
\end{array}
$$

I can move 615 cheese cubes.

Add or subtract.

①
$$
\begin{array}{r}
3\ 2\ 4 \\
+\ 1\ 8\ 3 \\
\hline
\end{array}
$$

②
$$
\begin{array}{r}
4\ 6\ 3 \\
+\ 2\ 8\ 7 \\
\hline
\end{array}
$$

③
$$
\begin{array}{r}
5\ 0\ 6 \\
-\ 2\ 7\ 7 \\
\hline
\end{array}
$$

④
$$
\begin{array}{r}
9\ 8\ 4 \\
-\ 3\ 9\ 9 \\
\hline
\end{array}
$$

⑤
$$
\begin{array}{r}
7\ 2\ 1 \\
-\ 4\ 6\ 8 \\
\hline
\end{array}
$$

⑥
$$
\begin{array}{r}
3\ 7\ 4 \\
+\ 5\ 3\ 3 \\
\hline
\end{array}
$$

⑦ 65 + 708 = _____

⑧ 217 – 94 = _____

Do the subtraction. Then check the answers.

⑨
$$
\begin{array}{r}
5\ 2\ 4 \\
-\ 1\ 6\ 2 \\
\hline
\end{array}
$$

Check
$$
+\ \underline{}
$$

⑩
$$
\begin{array}{r}
2\ 0\ 0 \\
-\ 1\ 5\ 4 \\
\hline
\end{array}
$$

Check
$$
+\ \underline{}
$$

⑪
$$
\begin{array}{r}
4\ 0\ 5 \\
-\ 1\ 7\ 3 \\
\hline
\end{array}
$$

Check
$$
+\ \underline{}
$$

⑫
$$
\begin{array}{r}
3\ 7\ 1 \\
-\ 3\ 1\ 8 \\
\hline
\end{array}
$$

Check
$$
+\ \underline{}
$$

ISBN: 978-1-897164-31-0

Round each number to the nearest hundred. Estimate. Then find the exact answer.

⑬
```
   3 9 4
 + 2 1 9
```
Estimate
```
   4 0 0
 + 2 0 0
```

⑭
```
   7 0 6
 +   9 2
```
Estimate

⑮
```
   8 2 7
 - 1 8 3
```
Estimate

⑯
```
   5 8 6
 - 3 2 8
```
Estimate

Find the sum and difference of each pair of numbers.

⑰ 319   254

Sum   Difference

⑱ 608   73

Sum   Difference

⑲ Sum ———— Difference

462
353

⑳ Sum ———— Difference

224
537

㉑ Sum ———— Difference

176
413

㉒ Sum ———— Difference

821
117

ISBN: 978-1-897164-31-0

Relating addition and subtraction:

$125 + 239 = 364$ $364 - 125 = 239$

$239 + 125 = 364$ $364 - 239 = 125$

125, 239, and 364 are in a family.

Use the given number sentences to find the answers.

㉓ $84 + 237 = 321$

a. $237 + 84 =$ _____

b. $321 - 84 =$ _____

㉔ $503 - 276 = 227$

a. $227 + 276 =$ _____

b. $503 - 227 =$ _____

㉕ $413 - 165 = 248$

a. $165 + 248 =$ _____

b. $413 - 248 =$ _____

㉖ $188 + 547 = 735$

a. $547 + 188 =$ _____

b. $735 - 547 =$ _____

Help the children complete their tables. Then fill in the blanks.

㉗ **Tina's Score**

	1st Round	2nd Round	Total
A	263 points	points	503 points
B	177 points	413 points	points
C	points	316 points	497 points

㉘ **Matthew's Score**

	1st Round	2nd Round	Total
A	points	164 points	471 points
B	525 points	76 points	points
C	367 points	points	604 points

I got my highest score in _____ .

I got my highest score in _____ .

ISBN: 978-1-897164-31-0

Solve the problems.

No. of Pizzas Sold		
	Pepperoni	Vegetarian
MON	218	182
TUE	174	203

㉙ How many pepperoni pizzas were sold on Monday and Tuesday?

_____ = _____

_____ pepperoni pizzas

㉚ How many vegetarian pizzas were sold on Monday and Tuesday?

_____ = _____

_____ vegetarian pizzas

We have pizzas in 2 sizes: large and small.

㉛ 79 small vegetarian pizzas were sold on Monday. How many large vegetarian pizzas were sold on that day?

_____ = _____

_____ large vegetarian pizzas

㉜ How many more vegetarian pizzas than pepperoni pizzas were sold on Tuesday?

_____ = _____

_____ more

㉝ *I have 154 slices of pizza. If I give 68 slices to my friends, how many slices of pizza will I have left?*

_____ = _____

_____ slices of pizza

ISBN: 978-1-897164-31-0

Length and Distance

See, we are both about 1 m tall.

You're not quite 1 m tall.

- Estimate, measure, and record length, height, and distance, using standard units such as centimetre, metre, and kilometre.

- Choose the most appropriate standard unit to measure length, height, and distance.

- Compare and order objects, using attributes measured in centimetres or metres.

Choose the best units to do the measurement.
Write "km", "m", or "cm" in the circles.

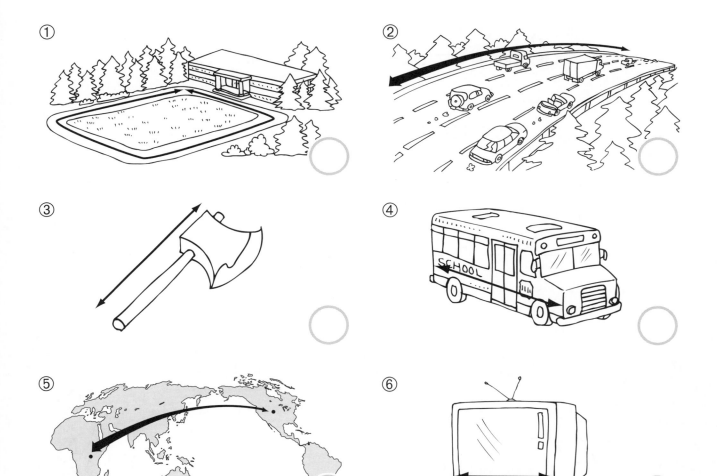

① ② ③ ④ ⑤ ⑥

ISBN: 978-1-897164-31-0

Fill in the blanks with "km", "m", or "cm" to complete the sentences.

⑦  The length of a ball of yarn is about 36 _____ .

⑧ The thickness of a book is about 3 _____ .

⑨ The distance between Toronto and New York is about 550 _____ .

⑩ Uncle Tim is shorter than 2 _____ .

⑪ Lucy found an earthworm in her backyard. It was about 12 _____ long.

Estimate the length of each line. Then measure and record the actual measurement. Use the given words if needed.

⑫

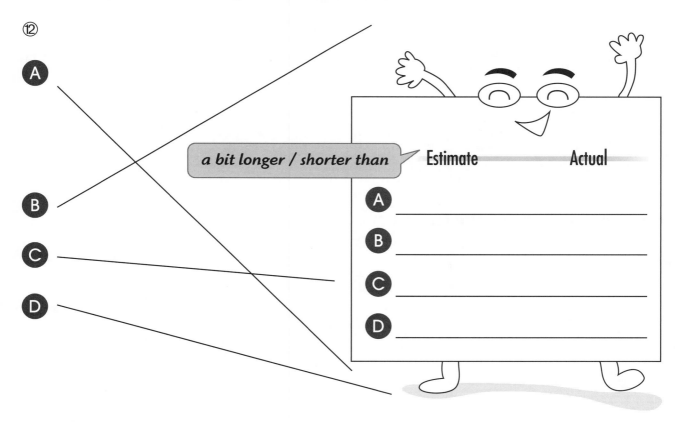

A
B
C
D

a bit longer / shorter than

Estimate   Actual

A _____

B _____

C _____

D _____

ISBN: 978-1-897164-31-0

Measure and record the length or height of each thing. Then draw and record the measurement of each item.

⑬

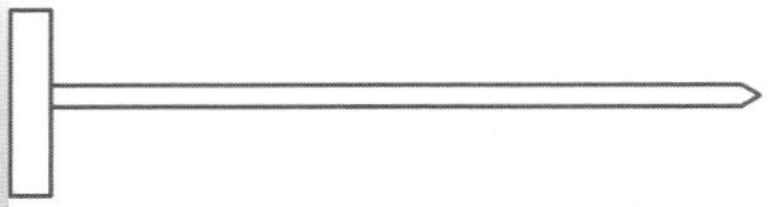

about _____ long

Draw a pencil that is 2 cm longer than the nail.

about _____ long

⑭ Ⓐ Ⓑ

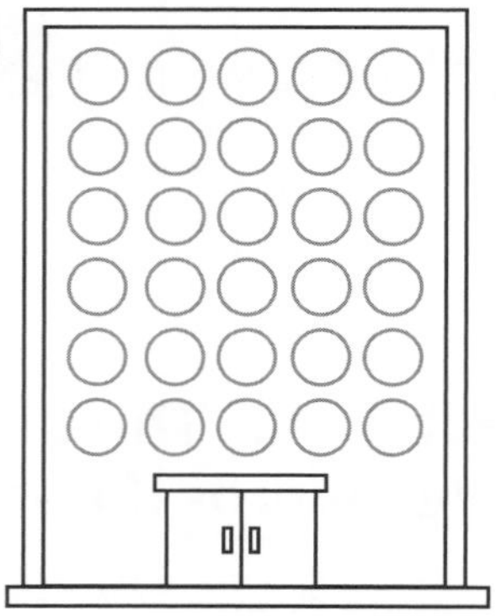

about _____ high   about _____ high   about _____ high

Draw a tree that is taller than A but shorter than B.

Measure and record the length of each line in centimetres.

⑮ Ⓐ

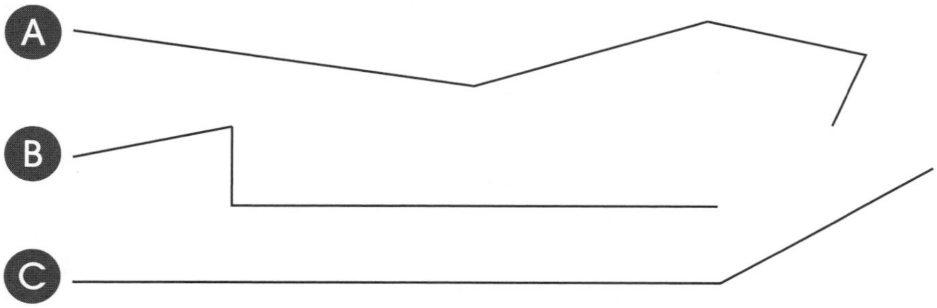

Ⓑ

Ⓒ

Length

Ⓐ _____

Ⓑ _____

Ⓒ _____

ISBN: 978-1-897164-31-0

Look at the diagram. Find the lengths of the routes. Then draw lines on the diagram and answer the questions.

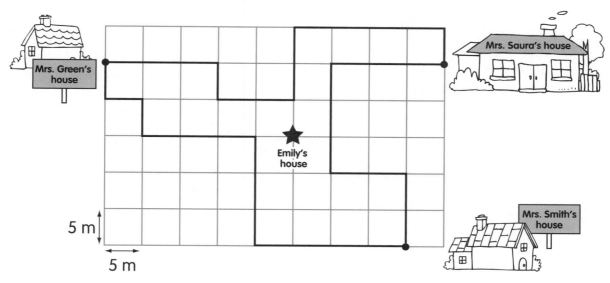

16 a. From Mrs. Green's house to Mrs. Saura's house: _____ m

b. From Mrs. Green's house to Mrs. Smith's house: _____ m

c. From Mrs. Saura's house to Mrs. Smith's house: _____ m

17 a.

Use a red pen to draw a new route on the diagram to show Mrs. Green the shortest route she can take from her house to Mrs. Saura's house.

b. The length of the route is _____ m.

18 a.

Use a green pen to draw a new route on the diagram to show Mrs. Smith the shortest route she can take from her house to Mrs. Saura's house.

b. The length of the route is _____ m.

19

I want to visit one of my aunts who is living closest to me. Who am I going to visit?

_____

ISBN: 978-1-897164-31-0

Perimeter and Area

- Understand the meaning of perimeter and area.
- Estimate, measure, and record the perimeter of 2-D shapes.
- Estimate, measure, and record the area of shapes.

> The perimeter of the mat is about 150 cm.

> The area of the mat is about the same as the total of 9 tiles.

Use a red pen to trace the perimeter of each shape.

① 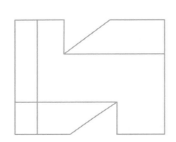 ② 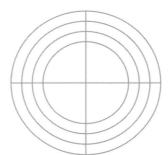 ③

Find the perimeter of each shape.

④

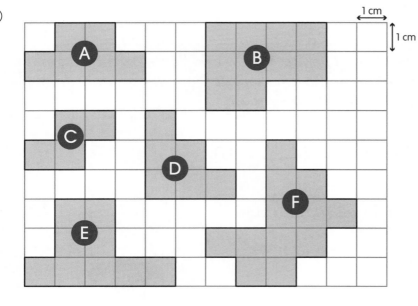

1 cm
1 cm

	Perimeter
A	
B	
C	
D	
E	
F	

ISBN: 978-1-897164-31-0

Estimate the perimeter of each shape. Then measure and record the actual perimeter.

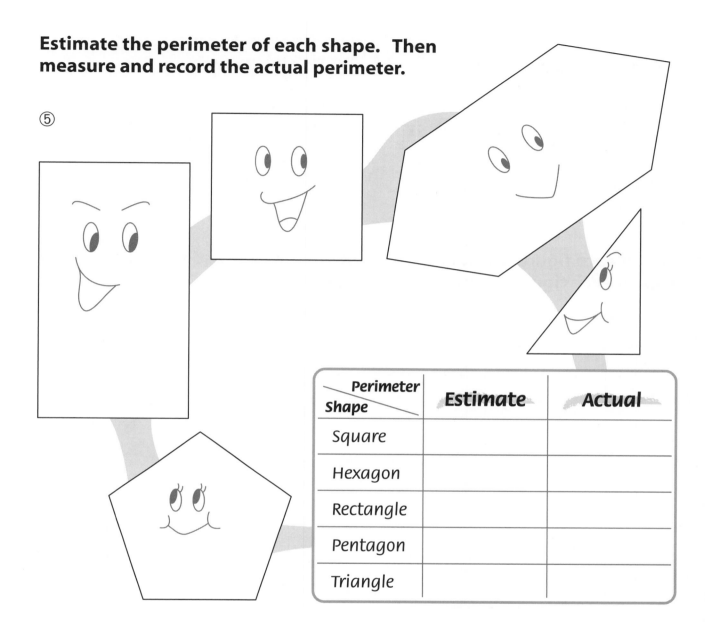

⑤

Perimeter / Shape	Estimate	Actual
Square		
Hexagon		
Rectangle		
Pentagon		
Triangle		

Draw the shapes on the grid.

⑥

Draw a square with a perimeter of 12 cm and a rectangle with a perimeter of 14 cm.

ISBN: 978-1-897164-31-0

Combine the parts to find areas.

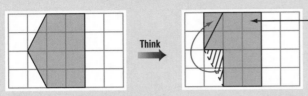

Think ➡

Cut out the part with stripes and put it to a place that can form squares. Then count the number of squares in the combined figure.

The area of this figure is 10 ☐ .

Colour each figure. Draw lines to complete the grid. Estimate and find the area of each figure. Then answer the questions.

⑦

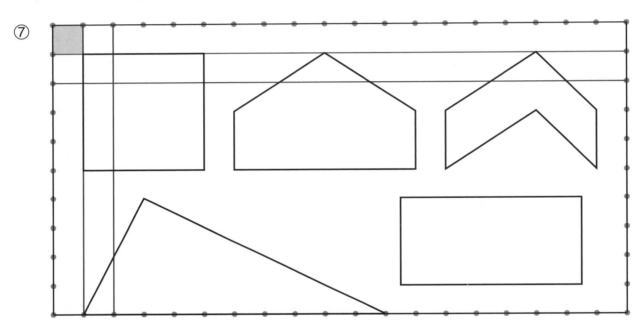

⑧

Area Figure	Estimate	Actual
Square		
Pentagon		
Hexagon		
Triangle		
Rectangle		

⑨ Which figure has the greatest area?

_____

⑩ If the square is cut into two identical triangles, what is the area of each triangle?

_____ ☐

ISBN: 978-1-897164-31-0

Draw the shapes on the grid.

⑪

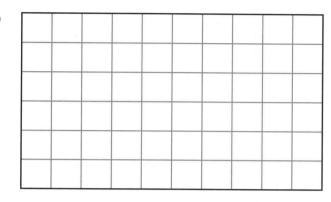

Draw a square with an area of 4 ☐ and a rectangle with an area of 15 ☐ .

The children use two different grids to measure the area of a placemat. Help them record the measurements. Then answer the questions.

⑫

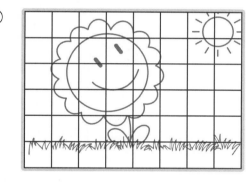

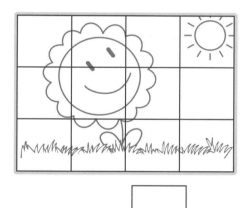

_____ ☐

_____ ☐

⑬ The greater the area of a unit, the smaller / greater the number of units used to cover a surface.

⑭

How many triangles are needed to cover the placemat?

_____ ◺

ISBN: 978-1-897164-31-0

You finished a plate of French fries in 2 minutes.

Start
05:42

Finish
05:44

Time and Temperature

- Read and write time in 12-hour notation.
- Find time intervals.
- Read water and air temperatures to the nearest degree Celsius.

Fill in the blanks to tell the times in 2 ways.

① 3 : _____

_____ min past 3

② _____ : 40

20 min to _____

③ 8 : _____

_____ min past 8

Tell the times in 2 ways.

 ④

A _____ ;

_____

B _____ ;

_____

C _____ ; _____

D _____ ; _____

E _____ ; _____

ISBN: 978-1-897164-31-0

Match the clocks with the times in words. Write the letters.

A 8:23

⑤ ____ Thirty-three minutes after two o'clock

B 2:33

____ Twenty-three minutes after eight o'clock

C 3:23

____ Twelve minutes after three o'clock

D 2:58

____ Fifty-eight minutes after two o'clock

____ Twenty-three minutes after three o'clock

E 12:08

____ *Eight minutes after twelve o'clock*

F 3:12

Help Jason write the times to complete his schedule. Then put his activities in order from 1 to 5.

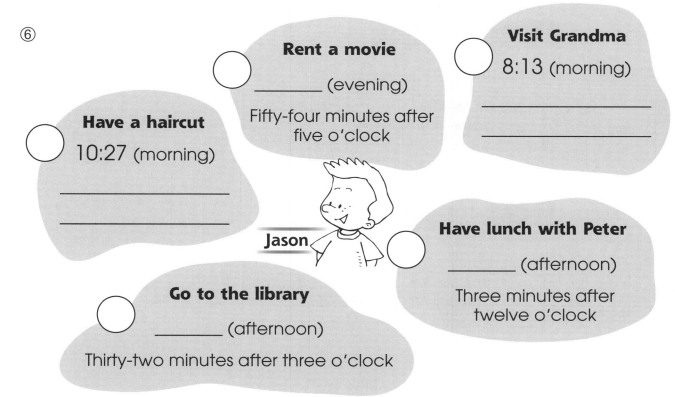

⑥

Rent a movie

○ _____ (evening)

Fifty-four minutes after five o'clock

Visit Grandma

○ 8:13 (morning)

_____

_____

Have a haircut

○ 10:27 (morning)

_____

_____

Jason

Have lunch with Peter

○ _____ (afternoon)

Three minutes after twelve o'clock

Go to the library

○ _____ (afternoon)

Thirty-two minutes after three o'clock

ISBN: 978-1-897164-31-0

You can use **subtraction** to find time intervals.

e.g.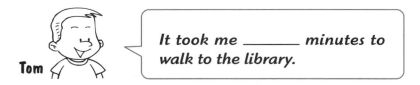

Think:

$$\begin{array}{r} 4\ 1 \\ -\ 2\ 6 \\ \hline 1\ 5 \end{array}$$

The time interval is 15 minutes.

See how long it took each child to go to the library. Find the time taken. Then answer the question.

⑦ From **9:14** to **9:53**

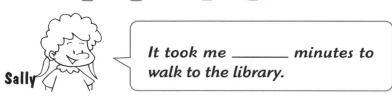

Tom: *It took me _____ minutes to walk to the library.*

___ − ___

⑧ From **11:08** to **11:21**

Sally: *It took me _____ minutes to walk to the library.*

___ − ___

⑨ From **3:27** to **3:39**

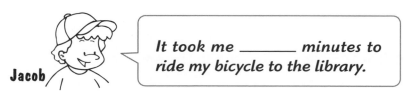

Jacob: *It took me _____ minutes to ride my bicycle to the library.*

___ − ___

⑩ Who lives closest to the library? _____

ISBN: 978-1-897164-31-0

Water Temperature:

- Water freezes at 0°C.
- Water boils at 100°C.

The air temperature on a warm day is about 20°C, but water at 20°C feels cool. I like to have a hot drink at 45°C.

Colour the thermometers to show the temperatures. Then match the thermometers with the correct pictures. Write the letters.

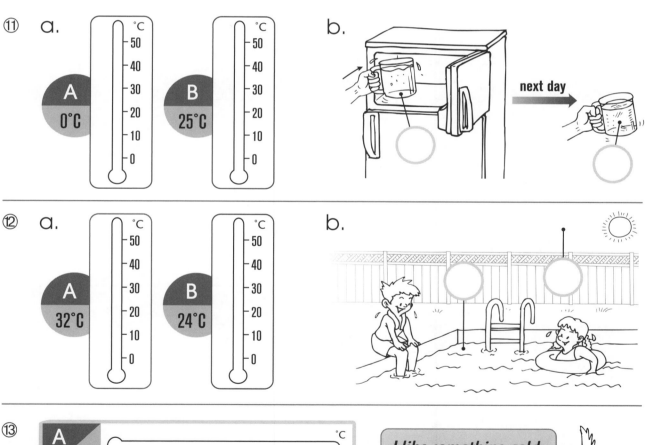

⑪ a.

A 0°C

B 25°C

b.

next day

⑫ a.

A 32°C

B 24°C

b.

⑬

A 16°C

B 46°C

I like something cold.

ISBN: 978-1-897164-31-0

Money

- Describe the relationships between coins and bills up to $10.

- Estimate and write money amounts up to $10.

- Add money amounts to make purchases up to $10.

I have 10 dollars.

I have 5 toonies.

Don't you know that 10-dollar bill is the same as 5 toonies?

Check ✔ the correct number of coins or bills to match the highlighted amount.

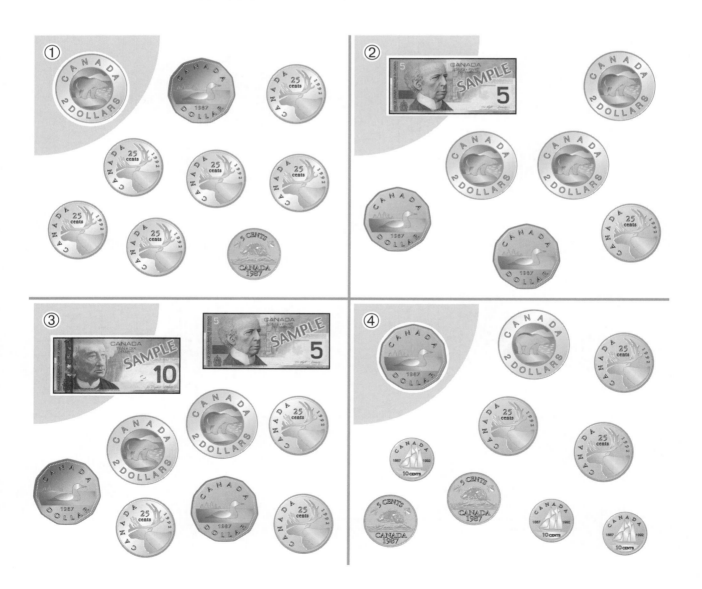

ISBN: 978-1-897164-31-0

Estimate and find the exact amount of money each child has. Then answer the questions.

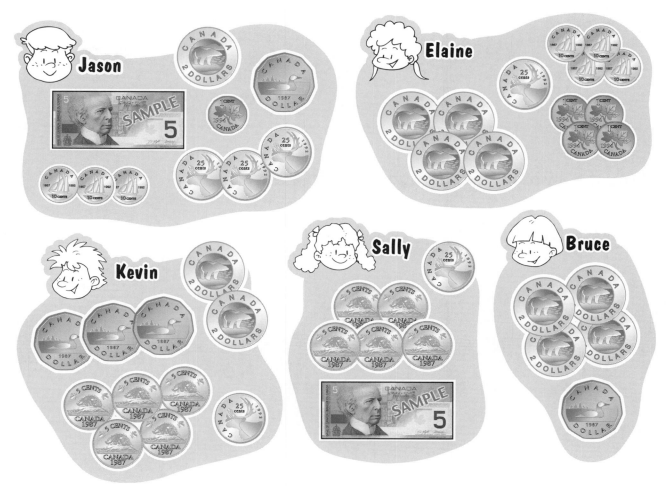

⑤

	Estimate		Actual	
Jason	dollars	cents	dollars	cents
Elaine				
Kevin				
Sally				
Bruce				

⑥ Who has the most money? _____

⑦ Who has the least money? _____

ISBN: 978-1-897164-31-0

Ways to write the amount:

Here is 3 dollars 36 cents.

dollars ←┐ ┌→ cents

3 dollars 36 cents = **$3.36**

There are 100 cents in 1 dollar.

Write the amount in each piggy bank in 2 ways.

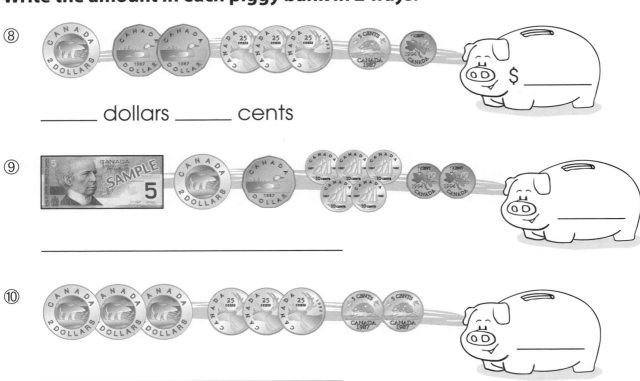

⑧ $ _____

_____ dollars _____ cents

⑨ _____

⑩ _____

Fill in the blanks.

⑪ **245 cents**

= 200 cents and ____ cents

= ____ dollars and ____ cents

= $ _____

⑫ **408 cents**

= ____ cents and 8 cents

= ____ dollars and ____ cents

= $ _____

ISBN: 978-1-897164-31-0

Draw the fewest bills and coins to show the cost of each robot.

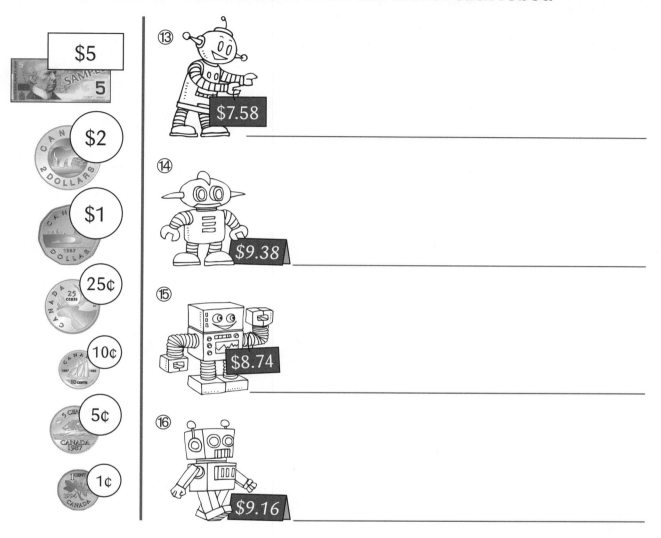

⑬ $7.58 _____

⑭ $9.38 _____

⑮ $8.74 _____

⑯ $9.16 _____

Read what the girl says. Draw the fewest bills and coins to show the money that she has.

⑰

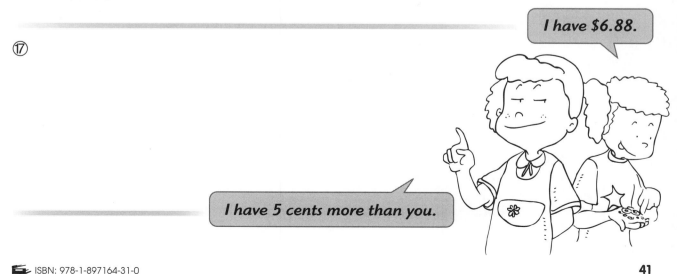

I have $6.88.

I have 5 cents more than you.

ISBN: 978-1-897164-31-0

$5 = 4 dollars
100 cents

Addition and Subtraction with Money

- Add and subtract money amounts to make purchases and changes up to $10.
- Solve money problems.

My change is $2.51, isn't it?

$2.49

$5

dollar	cent
4	100
− 2	49
2	51

Look at the pictures. Find the costs and answer the question.

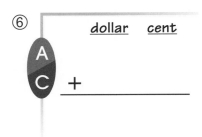

A $3.21

B $2.38

C $3.27

D $4.49

①

A
B
dollar	cent
+ _____

②

B
C
dollar	cent
+ _____

③

A
D
dollar	cent
+ _____

④

C
D
dollar	cent
+ _____

⑤

B
D
dollar	cent
+ _____

⑥
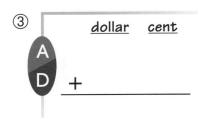
A
C
dollar	cent
+ _____

⑦

Which pair of toys costs the most?

_____

ISBN: 978-1-897164-31-0

Look at the toys on the previous page. Find how much each child pays and which toy he wants. Then find the change.

⑧ John pays $ _____ for Ⓐ .

dollar cent

_ _____ **Change: $** _____

⑨ Kenny pays $ _____ for Ⓒ .

dollar cent

_ _____ **Change: $** _____

⑩ Louis pays $ _____ for Ⓑ .

dollar cent

_ _____ **Change: $** _____

⑪ Frankie pays $ _____ for Ⓓ .

dollar cent

_ _____ **Change: $** _____

ISBN: 978-1-897164-31-0

Adding money:

dollar	cent
1	
3	87 ←
+ 1	49
5	36

87 + 49 = 136
Carry 100 cents to the dollar column.

$3.87 + $1.49
= **$5.36**

Subtracting money:

dollar	cent
4	129
5̶	2̶9̶ ←
− 1	68
3	61

Borrow 1 from the dollar column.
100 + 29 = 129

$5.29 − $1.68
= **$3.61**

$1 = 100¢

Fill in the missing information on each receipt.

$1.88

Puzzle
$4.89

Crackers Crackers
$3.19

$2.16

⑫ **R & A Superstore**

Puzzle	$ _____
Crackers	$ _____
Total	$ _____
CASH	$ 10.00
CHANGE	$

⑬ **R & A Superstore**

Detergent	$ _____
Bread	$ _____
Total	$ _____
CASH	$
CHANGE	$ 0.21

⑭ **R & A Superstore**

Crackers	$ _____
Bread	$ _____
Total	$ _____
CASH	$ 6.00
CHANGE	$

⑮ **R & A Superstore**

Detergent	$ _____
Detergent	$ _____
Total	$ _____
CASH	$
CHANGE	$ 1.24

⑯ **R & A Superstore**

Bread	$ _____
_____	$ _____
Total	$ 7.05
CASH	$
CHANGE	$ 0.20

⑰ **R & A Superstore**

Crackers	$ _____
_____	$ _____
Total	$ 5.07
CASH	$
CHANGE	$ 4.93

ISBN: 978-1-897164-31-0

Solve the problems.

⑱ Mrs. Smith pays $5 for a book that costs $3.77. What is her change?

$ _____

⑲ Jordan has $4.25. If he wants to buy a key chain that costs $6.42, how much more does he need?

$ _____

⑳ A box of chocolates costs $3.66. How much do 2 boxes of chocolates cost?

$ _____

㉑ Adam has $5.27 and his brother has $3.64. How much do the boys have in all?

$ _____

㉒

I have $9.50. Do you think I have enough money to buy 2 sundaes for my parents? If not, how much more do I need?

Special

$4.77

_____

ISBN: 978-1-897164-31-0

Capacity and Mass

- Estimate, measure, and record the capacity of containers using litres or parts of a litre.
- Estimate, measure, and record the mass of objects using kilograms or parts of a kilogram.

> *It's getting heavier and heavier.*

> It can hold 5 L of sand.

Sort the containers. Then answer the questions.

① 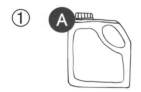 **A**   **B**   **C**

 D   **E**    **F**

 **G**   **H**    **I**

- about 1 L:

  _____

- less than 1 L:

  _____

- more than 1 L:

  _____

② Which container holds the most?   _____

③ Which container holds the least?   _____

Draw the water level in each container.

④
- 4 L
- 3
- 2
- 1

3 L

⑤
- 5 L
- 4
- 3
- 2
- 1

4 L

⑥
- 10 L
- 8
- 6
- 4
- 2

5 L

ISBN: 978-1-897164-31-0

Which capacity seems reasonable? Circle the correct answer.

⑦

about 50 L

more than 200 L

⑧

less than 5 L

about 100 L

⑨

less than 1 L

about 10 L

Each container has a capacity of 1 L. Write how much water is in each container with the given words.

⑩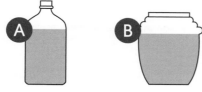

a quarter   half   three quarters

A _____ of a litre

B _____

C _____

D _____

Look at the containers. Fill in the blanks.

⑪ The juice box can hold _____ of a litre of juice. It takes about _____ juice boxes of water to fill up the ice cream tub.

250 mL   1 L

⑫ The big water bottle can hold _____ of water. It takes about _____ pails of water to fill up the big water bottle.

50 L   2 L

ISBN: 978-1-897164-31-0

Write the mass of each object. Then answer the questions.

⑬

▬▬ **Mass** ▬▬

Flour: _____

Pumpkin: _____

Rock: _____

Frog: _____

Watermelon: _____

Tin soldier: _____

⑭ The _____ and the _____ have the same weight.

⑮ _____ bags of flour are needed to balance the frog.

⑯ Draw the correct number of | 1 kg | to balance the objects.

ISBN: 978-1-897164-31-0

Each container can hold 1 kg of sugar. Write how much sugar is in each container with the given words.

a quarter   half   three quarters

⑰

Ⓐ   Ⓑ

Ⓒ   Ⓓ

Ⓐ _____ of a kilogram

Ⓑ _____

Ⓒ _____

Ⓓ _____

Look at the pictures. Fill in the blanks.

⑱ a. Half of a watermelon weighs _____ kg.

   b. The whole watermelon weighs _____ kg.

   c. If Jason cuts the half watermelon in half again, each piece weighs _____ kg.

⑲ a. 4 boxes of chocolates weigh _____ kg.

   b. Each box of chocolates weighs _____ than 1 kg.

   c. *If I can lift 10 kg at a time, how many boxes of chocolates can I lift at one go?*

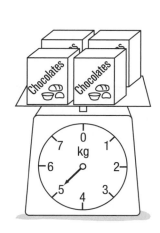

_____ boxes of chocolates

ISBN: 978-1-897164-31-0

Multiplication (1)

- Understand multiplication as repeated addition.
- Multiply to 7 x 7.
- Multiply a 1-digit number by 8 or 9 with the help of pictures.

$$\begin{array}{r} 4 \\ \times\ 5 \\ \hline 2\ 0 \end{array}$$

Give back all 20 rings to me!

Circle the objects. Then fill in the blanks.

① Circle every 3 dolphins.

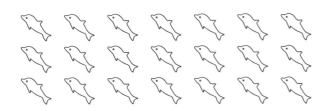

3 + 3 + 3 + 3 + _____

= ____ groups of 3

= ____ x 3

= _____

② Circle every 4 🐟 .

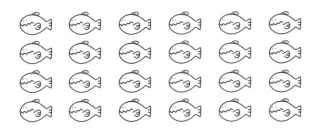

4 + _____

= ____ groups of ____

= ____ x ____

= _____

③ Circle every 5 🐢 .

5 + _____

= ____ groups of ____

= ____ x ____

= _____

ISBN: 978-1-897164-31-0

Look at the pictures.   Fill in the blanks.

④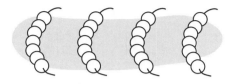

_____ groups of 7

= _____ times 7

= _____ x 7

= _____

⑤

_____ groups of 9

= _____ times 9

= _____ x 9

= _____

⑥

_____ groups of 5

= _____ times 5

= _____ x 5

= _____

⑦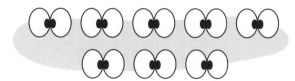

_____ groups of 2

= _____ times 2

= _____ x 2

= _____

Write a multiplication sentence to match each group of items.

⑧

_____ X _____ = _____

⑨

_____ X _____ = _____

⑩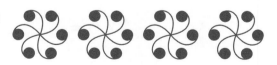

_____ X _____ = _____

⑪

_____ X _____ = _____

ISBN: 978-1-897164-31-0

Draw arrows to continue the patterns. Then count by 3's, 4's, or 7's to write the missing numbers.

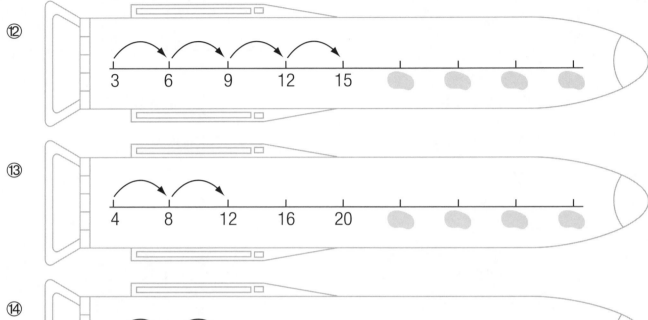

⑫ 3   6   9   12   15

⑬ 4   8   12   16   20

⑭ 7   14   21   28   35

Complete the multiplication tables.

⑮ 1 x 6 = _____
   2 x 6 = _____
   3 x 6 = _____
   4 x 6 = _____
   5 x 6 = _____
   6 x 6 = _____
   7 x 6 = _____
   8 x 6 = _____
   9 x 6 = _____

⑯ 1 x 2 = _____
   2 x 2 = _____
   3 x 2 = _____
   4 x 2 = _____
   5 x 2 = _____
   6 x 2 = _____
   7 x 2 = _____
   8 x 2 = _____
   9 x 2 = _____

⑰ 1 x 5 = _____
   2 x 5 = _____
   3 x 5 = _____
   4 x 5 = _____
   5 x 5 = _____
   6 x 5 = _____
   7 x 5 = _____
   8 x 5 = _____
   9 x 5 = _____

ISBN: 978-1-897164-31-0

Multiplication charts:

multiplication sign →

x	1	2	3	4	5	6	7
1							
2					10		
3							
4							
5		10					
6							
7							

A number from

2 **x** 5

5 **x** 2

Complete the multiplication chart. Then find the answers.

⑱

X	1	2	3	4	5	6	7
1	1	2				6	7
2		4	6				
3				12	15		
4	4				20		28
5	5	10					
6			18		30		
7	7			28			49

⑲ 4 x 6 = _____

⑳ 5 x 3 = _____

㉑ 2 x 7 = _____

㉒ 6 x 6 = _____

㉓ 4 x 5 = _____

㉔ 6 x 7 = _____

㉕

Lily, Louis, Michael, and I each have 6 lollipops. How many lollipops do we have in all?

_____ lollipops

 ISBN: 978-1-897164-31-0

Multiplication (2)

$$\begin{array}{r} 6 \\ \times\ 4 \\ \hline 2\ 4 \end{array}$$

- Do vertical multiplication.
- Use multiplication to solve problems.

> Bobby is balancing himself on 24 blocks.

Do the multiplication.

①
$$\begin{array}{r} 3 \\ \times\ 9 \\ \hline \end{array}$$

②
$$\begin{array}{r} 4 \\ \times\ 8 \\ \hline \end{array}$$

③
$$\begin{array}{r} 6 \\ \times\ 5 \\ \hline \end{array}$$

④
$$\begin{array}{r} 7 \\ \times\ 6 \\ \hline \end{array}$$

⑤
$$\begin{array}{r} 2 \\ \times\ 7 \\ \hline \end{array}$$

⑥
$$\begin{array}{r} 5 \\ \times\ 5 \\ \hline \end{array}$$

⑦
$$\begin{array}{r} 4 \\ \times\ 6 \\ \hline \end{array}$$

⑧
$$\begin{array}{r} 5 \\ \times\ 3 \\ \hline \end{array}$$

⑨
$$\begin{array}{r} 3 \\ \times\ 8 \\ \hline \end{array}$$

⑩
$$\begin{array}{r} 7 \\ \times\ 4 \\ \hline \end{array}$$

⑪
$$\begin{array}{r} 5 \\ \times\ 9 \\ \hline \end{array}$$

⑫
$$\begin{array}{r} 4 \\ \times\ 9 \\ \hline \end{array}$$

⑬
$$\begin{array}{r} 6 \\ \times\ 8 \\ \hline \end{array}$$

⑭
$$\begin{array}{r} 7 \\ \times\ 5 \\ \hline \end{array}$$

Fill in the missing numbers.

⑮
$$\begin{array}{r} 3 \\ \times\ \\ \hline 2\ 4 \end{array}$$

⑯
$$\begin{array}{r} 7 \\ \times\ \\ \hline 4\ 9 \end{array}$$

⑰
$$\begin{array}{r} 6 \\ \times\ \\ \hline 1\ 8 \end{array}$$

⑱
$$\begin{array}{r} 4 \\ \times\ \\ \hline 2\ 8 \end{array}$$

ISBN: 978-1-897164-31-0

See how many candies the children get if they trade these things with Sally. Help the children solve the problems.

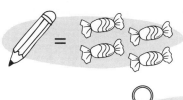 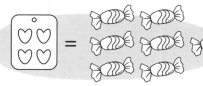

Sally

⑲ Mary trades 6 pencils for candies. How many candies does she get?

_____ candies

X_____

⑳ John trades 3 key chains for candies. How many candies does he get?

_____ candies

_____

㉑ Lily has 4 sheets of stickers. If she wants to trade them for candies, how many candies will she get?

_____ candies

_____

㉒ Katie wants to trade either 5 sheets of stickers or 6 key chains for candies. Which should she trade for more candies?

_____   _____

_____

ISBN: 978-1-897164-31-0

Read what the children say. Solve the problems.

㉓ a.
> How many apples are there in 4 baskets?

_____ apples

b.
> Each apple costs 7¢. How much does a basket of apples cost?

_____ ¢

㉔ a.
> How many coins are there on 3 pages?

_____ coins

b.
> 1 coin weighs the same as 5 paper clips. How heavy are the coins on each page?

_____ paper clips

㉕ a.
> There are 6 muffins in a box. How many muffins are there in 5 boxes?

_____ muffins

b.
> There are 7 members in my family. If each member eats 2 muffins a day, how many muffins do we eat every day?

_____ muffins

ISBN: 978-1-897164-31-0

Help the girls find how many points they get. Complete the table. Then answer the questions.

Each of us can pick 6 cards.

7 points   **5 points**   **4 points**

㉖

					Total
Tina	4 🐰	____ points	2 🐵	____ points	____ points
Eva	2 🐑	____ points	4 🐵	____ points	____ points
Susan	5 🐰	____ points	1 🐑	____ points	____ points

㉗   Who has the most points?   _____

㉘   Who has the fewest points?   _____

㉙   If Eva picks 2 🐰 instead of 2 🐑, will she be the winner?   _____

㉚

I have taken 2 🐵 from Eva. How many points does Eva have now?

_____ points

ISBN: 978-1-897164-31-0

You've used all 28 beads to make 4 bracelets with 7 beads each.

Division (1)

- Divide a set of objects into groups of a certain number.
- Divide a set of objects into equal shares.
- Solve division problems.

Circle the items. Then fill in the blanks.

① Circle every 3 apples.

There are _____ apples. If I eat 3 apples a day, it will take me _____ days to finish all of them.

② Circle every 7 cherries.

There are _____ cherries. If there are 7 cherries in a group, there will be _____ groups in all.

③ Circle every 5 peanuts.

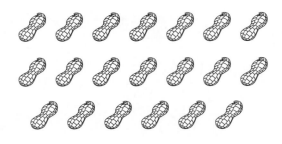

There are _____ peanuts. If I put 5 peanuts in a bag, I will need _____ bags in all.

ISBN: 978-1-897164-31-0

Draw the things in the spaces provided. Then fill in the blanks.

④   Put 28 nails equally into 4 boxes.

Put 1 nail into a box at a time and continue until you've put in all 28 nails.

There are _____ nails in a box.

⑤   Put 12 fish equally into 6 nets.

There are _____ fish in each net.

⑥   Put 15 potatoes equally into 5 pots.

There are _____ potatoes in each pot.

⑦   Give 18 flowers equally to 3 bees.

Each bee has _____ flowers.

ISBN: 978-1-897164-31-0

Draw the missing items. Then fill in the blanks.

⑧ **24 fish in 4 rows**

There are ___ fish in each row.

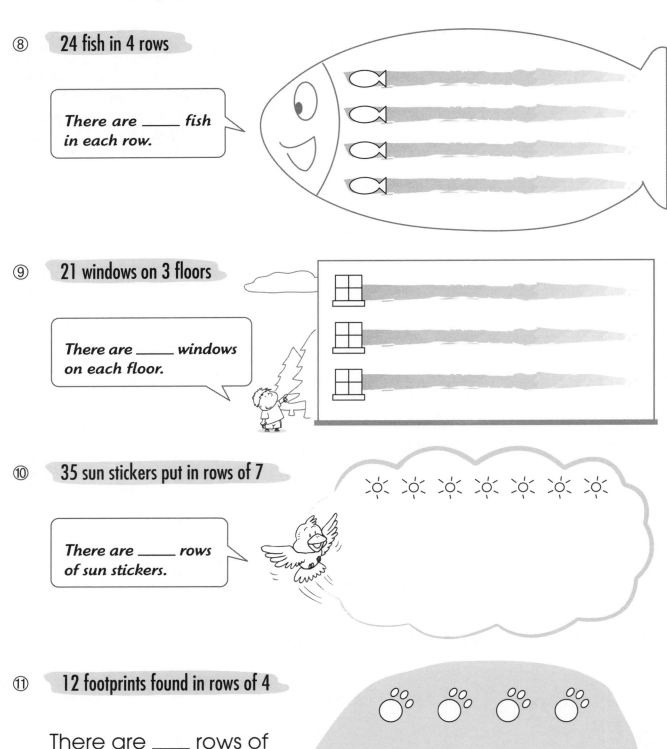

⑨ **21 windows on 3 floors**

There are ___ windows on each floor.

⑩ **35 sun stickers put in rows of 7**

There are ___ rows of sun stickers.

⑪ **12 footprints found in rows of 4**

There are ___ rows of footprints.

ISBN: 978-1-897164-31-0

Look at the pictures. Fill in the blanks.

⑫ a. Mrs. Smith has _____ rings.

b. If Mrs. Smith puts 5 rings in a box, she needs _____ boxes in all.

c. If she puts 3 rings in a box, she needs _____ boxes in all.

Mrs. Smith's rings

⑬ a. Bobby has _____ bones.

b. If Bobby puts 8 bones in a hole, he needs _____ holes in all.

c. If Bobby eats 4 bones a day, it will take him _____ days to finish all the bones.

Bobby's bones

Read what Linda says. Check ✔ the correct letter.

⑭

> *I will share my candies with my 2 friends. Each of us will get 9 candies. Which group of candies is mine?*

Ⓐ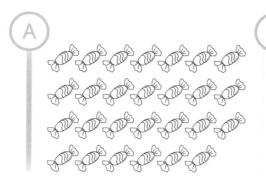

Ⓑ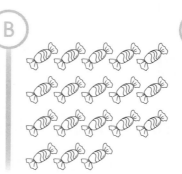

Ⓒ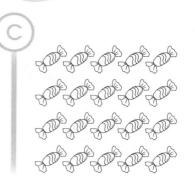

ISBN: 978-1-897164-31-0

Write the numbers where the balloons are. Then answer the questions.

① a.

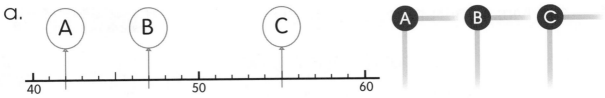

b.   Which number will be 50 when it is rounded
     to the nearest 10?   _____

c.   A number that is 10 more than C   _____

② a.

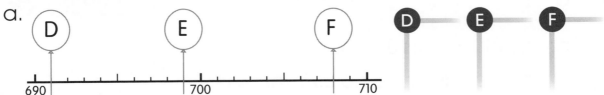

b.   Which number has a 9 in both ones and
     tens columns?   _____

c.   A number that is 100 less than D   _____

Write the numbers.

③   twenty-nine   _____   ④   seventy-four   _____

⑤

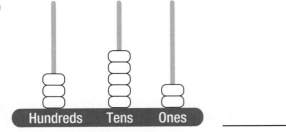

_____

⑥

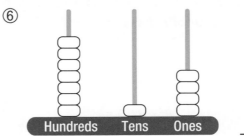

_____

⑦   439 = _____ hundreds _____ tens _____ ones

⑧   586 = _____ hundreds _____ tens _____ ones

               ISBN: 978-1-897164-31-0

Find the answers.

⑨
```
    4 6
+   1 9
_____
```

⑩
```
    7 3
–   4 8
_____
```

⑪
```
      6
+   6 5
_____
```

⑫
```
    3 1 5
+   2 6 8
_____
```

⑬
```
    5 0 0
–   2 7 4
_____
```

⑭
```
    4 4 2
–   1 3 9
_____
```

⑮ 207 + 313 = _____

⑯ 45 – 28 = _____

⑰ 163 – 46 = _____

⑱ 532 + 88 = _____

⑲ 310 – 44 = _____

⑳ 104 – 56 = _____

Solve the problems.

㉑ If Jill fills up the jar with candies, how many candies will be left in the bag?

_____ = _____

_____ candies

㉒ How many candies are there in a bag and a jar?

_____ = _____   _____ candies

㉓ Jill has two bags of candies. How many candies does she have in all?

_____ = _____   _____ candies

㉔ If Jill gives 110 candies to her sister, how many candies will she have left?

_____ = _____   _____ candies

ISBN: 978-1-897164-31-0

Do the subtraction. Then check the answers.

㉕
```
  3 3 4
- 2 7 9
```
Check

㉖
```
  4 1 7
- 1 0 8
```
Check

㉗
```
  6 0 0
- 4 6 3
```
Check

㉘
```
  8 0 3
- 7 9 5
```
Check

Measure and circle the correct word to record the length of each line in centimetres. Then answer the questions.

㉙ A ————————————————————

 B

C

A   a bit   shorter / longer   than _____

B   exactly _____

C   a bit   shorter / longer   than _____

㉚ Which one is the longest?   _____

㉛ Draw a pencil which is about 1 cm shorter than .

ISBN: 978-1-897164-31-0

Find the perimeters or areas of the figures.

③②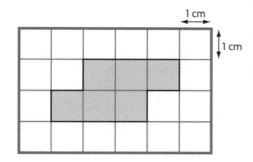

Perimeter: _____ cm

③③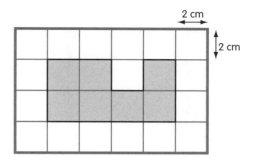

Perimeter: _____ cm

③④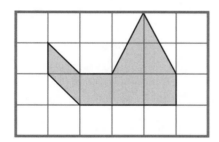

Area: _____ ☐

③⑤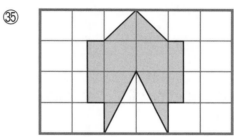

Area: _____ ☐

Write the times on the digital clocks. Then find the time intervals.

③⑥ **A**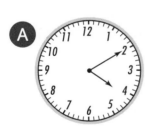

B
25 min to 5

C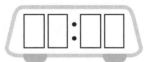
Fifty-one minutes after four o'clock

③⑦ From **A** to **B** : _____ min

_____

③⑧ From **B** to **C** : _____ min

_____

ISBN: 978-1-897164-31-0

Write the cost of each toy in 2 ways. Then solve the problems.

③⑨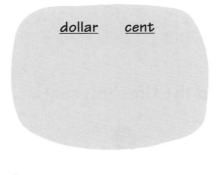

$ [   ] ; _____ dollars _____ cents

④⓪

$ [   ] ; _____ dollars _____ cents

④① How much do 2 robots cost?

dollar	cent

$ _____

④② Jill pays $7 for a pail. What is her change?

dollar	cent

$ _____

Each container has a capacity of 1 L. Colour the containers to show how much water they hold.

④③ three quarters of a litre

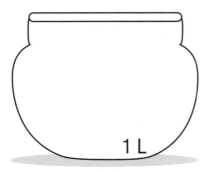

1 L

④④ half a litre

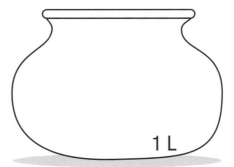

1 L

ISBN: 978-1-897164-31-0

Find the answers.

㊺
$$\begin{array}{r} 3 \\ \times\ 9 \\ \hline \end{array}$$

㊻
$$\begin{array}{r} 4 \\ \times\ 8 \\ \hline \end{array}$$

㊼
$$\begin{array}{r} 7 \\ \times\ 7 \\ \hline \end{array}$$

㊽ 2 x 6 = _____

㊾ 7 x 4 = _____

㊿ 5 x 3 = _____

51 4 x 5 = _____

52 9 x 2 = _____

53 8 x 7 = _____

54 Each box has 6 doughnuts. How many doughnuts are there in 5 boxes?

_____ = _____   _____ doughnuts

55 A pencil costs 7¢. How much do 9 pencils cost?

_____ = _____   _____ ¢

Draw the missing items. Then fill in the blanks.

56 28 girls in 7 rows

57 18 boys in rows of 3

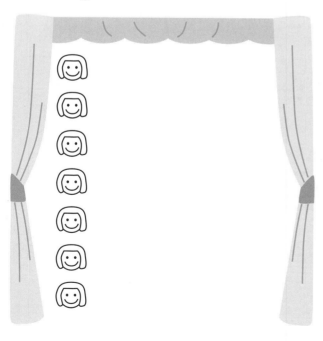

There are ____ girls in each row.   There are ____ rows of boys.

ISBN: 978-1-897164-31-0

Division (2)

> I've helped you put 13 lollipops equally on 4 stands and there's 1 left. So, I should keep it.

- Use division sign to write division sentences.
- Do long division and division with remainder.
- Solve division problems.

$13 \div 4 = 3R1$

See how Mrs. Green packs her muffins. Complete the division sentences.

① 20 muffins divided into groups of 4

$20 \div 4 =$ _____

There are _____ groups of 4.

② 15 muffins divided into groups of 5

$15 \div 5 =$ _____

There are _____ groups of 5.

③

> Each box holds 6 muffins. How many boxes do I need to hold 24 muffins?

 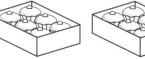 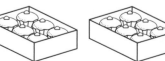 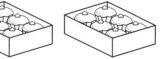

$24 \div 6 =$ _____

Mrs. Green needs _____ boxes in all.

ISBN: 978-1-897164-31-0

Colour the pictures. Then use long division to find the answers.

④ Jason colours every 3 balls with the same colour. If he has 18 balls, how many different colours does he use?

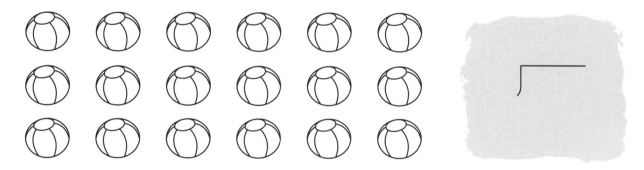

He uses _____ different colours.

⑤ Anita has 20 flowers. How many different colours does she use if she colours every 5 flowers the same colour?

She uses _____ different colours.

ISBN: 978-1-897164-31-0

Do the division.

⑥

$$5 \overline{)30}$$

⑦

$$8 \overline{)24}$$

⑧

$$2 \overline{)16}$$

⑨

$$7 \overline{)42}$$

⑩ $15 \div 3 = $ _____

⑪ $20 \div 4 = $ _____

⑫ $24 \div 6 = $ _____

⑬ $12 \div 4 = $ _____

⑭ $18 \div 6 = $ _____

⑮ $21 \div 3 = $ _____

⑯ $25 \div 5 = $ _____

⑰ $49 \div 7 = $ _____

⑱ $30 \div 6 = $ _____

Solve the problems.

⑲ May, Sam, and Ted share 27 cookies equally. How many cookies does each child have?

_____ cookies

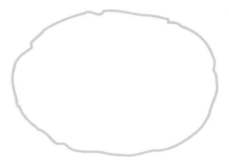

⑳ Each doll costs \$2. How many dolls can Linda buy with \$16?

_____ dolls

㉑ Mary has 30 stickers. If she puts every 5 stickers in a box, how many boxes does she need to hold all the stickers?

_____ boxes

ISBN: 978-1-897164-31-0

I have 13 apples. If I put every 2 apples on a plate, how many plates do I need? How many apples are left?

You need 6 plates. 1 apple is left.

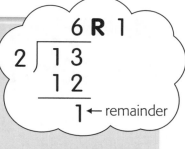

$$\begin{array}{r} 6\ \textbf{R}\ 1 \\ 2\overline{)\ 1\ 3} \\ 1\ 2 \\ \hline 1 \leftarrow \text{remainder} \end{array}$$

$13 \div 2 = \underline{\textbf{6R1}}$

Do the division.

㉒

$$4\overline{)\ 1\ 5} \quad \text{R} \underline{\quad}$$

㉓

$$3\overline{)\ 2\ 0} \quad \text{R} \underline{\quad}$$

㉔

$$7\overline{)\ 1\ 8} \quad \text{R} \underline{\quad}$$

㉕ $11 \div 5 = \underline{\hspace{2cm}}$

㉖ $19 \div 6 = \underline{\hspace{2cm}}$

㉗ $18 \div 4 = \underline{\hspace{2cm}}$

㉘ $14 \div 3 = \underline{\hspace{2cm}}$

Solve the problems.

㉙ Judy has 25 stickers. If she puts every 7 stickers in a bag, how many bags does she need? How many stickers are left?

$\underline{\hspace{1.5cm}} \div \underline{\hspace{1.5cm}} = \underline{\hspace{2cm}}$

She needs _____ bags. _____ stickers are left.

㉚

I want to share my candies with my two friends equally. How many candies does each of us get? How many candies are left?

$\underline{\hspace{1.5cm}} \div \underline{\hspace{1.5cm}} = \underline{\hspace{2cm}}$

Each gets _____ candies. _____ candies are left.

ISBN: 978-1-897164-31-0

Multiplication and Division

- Do multiplication and division.
- Understand the relationship between multiplication and division.
- Solve word problems.

> Each row has 3 cookies.
> 4 x 3 = 12

> No. of cookies that each of us has:
> 12 ÷ 2 = 6

> I've made 12 cookies.

> Each of us can have 6 cookies.

Find the answers.

①
$$\begin{array}{r} 3 \\ \times\ 6 \\ \hline \end{array}$$

②
$$\begin{array}{r} 4 \\ \times\ 9 \\ \hline \end{array}$$

③
$$\begin{array}{r} 5 \\ \times\ 7 \\ \hline \end{array}$$

④
$$\begin{array}{r} 2 \\ \times\ 8 \\ \hline \end{array}$$

⑤ $8\overline{)40}$

⑥ $5\overline{)41}$ R ___

⑦ $6\overline{)24}$

⑧ $4\overline{)36}$

⑨ $7\overline{)42}$

⑩ $3\overline{)20}$ R ___

⑪ 2 x 4 = _____

⑫ 6 x 6 = _____

⑬ 15 ÷ 4 = _____

⑭ 28 ÷ 7 = _____

⑮ 3 x 5 = _____

⑯ 8 x 6 = _____

⑰ 9 x 3 = _____

⑱ 32 ÷ 4 = _____

ISBN: 978-1-897164-31-0

Write a multiplication sentence and a division sentence to match each group of pictures.

⑲

_____ X _____ = _____

_____ ÷ _____ = _____

⑳

_____ X _____ = _____

_____ ÷ _____ = _____

㉑

_____ X _____ = _____

_____ ÷ _____ = _____

㉒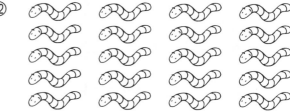

_____ X _____ = _____

_____ ÷ _____ = _____

Choose the correct numbers to write a multiplication sentence and a division sentence.

㉓

_____

_____

㉔

_____

_____

㉕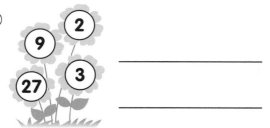

_____

_____

㉖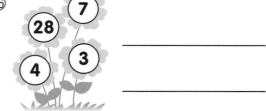

_____

_____

ISBN: 978-1-897164-31-0

Help the boys solve the problems. Check ✔ the correct number sentences and find the answers.

㉗

> *A big box can hold 6 muffins and a small box can hold 4. If Mrs. Smith has 7 small boxes of muffins, how many muffins does she have in all?*

Ⓐ 7 x 6 = _____   Ⓑ 7 x 4 = _____

She has _____ muffins in all.

㉘

> *How many big boxes are needed to hold 24 muffins?*

Ⓐ 24 ÷ 6 = _____   Ⓑ 24 ÷ 4 = _____

_____ big boxes are needed.

㉙

> *I have 6 green and 42 red marbles. How many marbles do I have in all?*

Ⓐ 42 ÷ 6 = _____   Ⓑ 42 – 6 = _____

Ⓒ 6 + 42 = _____   Ⓓ 42 x 6 = _____

Jason has _____ marbles in all.

㉚

> *If I put my marbles equally into 6 groups, how many marbles are there in each group?*

Ⓐ 42 ÷ 6 = _____   Ⓑ 6 x 6 = _____

Ⓒ 48 x 6 = _____   Ⓓ 48 ÷ 6 = _____

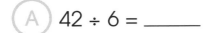

There are _____ marbles in each group.

ISBN: 978-1-897164-31-0

Solve the problems.

③① Each pumpkin costs $4. How much do 8 pumpkins cost?

$ _____

③② Each basket holds 7 apples. How many baskets are needed to hold 28 apples?

_____ baskets

③③ If Joey shares a box of 27 cards with 2 friends, how many cards will each child get?

_____ cards

③④ *A bag can hold 5 cookies. How many cookies are there in all in 7 bags?*

_____ = _____

_____ cookies

③⑤ *How many bags are needed to hold 49 cookies?*

_____ = _____

_____ bags

ISBN: 978-1-897164-31-0

Fractions

- Divide whole objects or sets of objects into equal parts.
- Identify the parts using fractional names.
- Compare and order fractions.

You have this and I have the rest.

What? I can only have one sixteenth of a pizza?

Draw lines to cut each shape into equal parts. Then do the colouring and fill in the blanks.

① **Cut it into 8 equal parts and colour 2 parts.**

Two _____ of the square is coloured.

② **Cut it into 6 equal parts and colour 5 parts.**

Five _____ of the hexagon is coloured.

③ **Cut it into 10 equal parts. Then colour 2 parts blue and 5 parts orange.**

Two _____ of the rectangle is blue and

five _____ is orange.

ISBN: 978-1-897164-31-0

Write a fraction to tell the shaded part in each figure.

④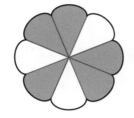

_____ eighths

⑤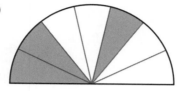

_____

⑥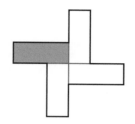

_____

⑦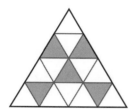

_____

⑧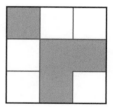

_____

⑨

_____

Write a fraction to tell the shaded animals in each group.

⑩

_____

⑪

_____

⑫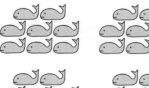

_____

⑬

_____

ISBN: 978-1-897164-31-0

Draw lines to divide the items in each group into equal parts. Then colour the parts and fill in the blanks with fractional names.

⑭

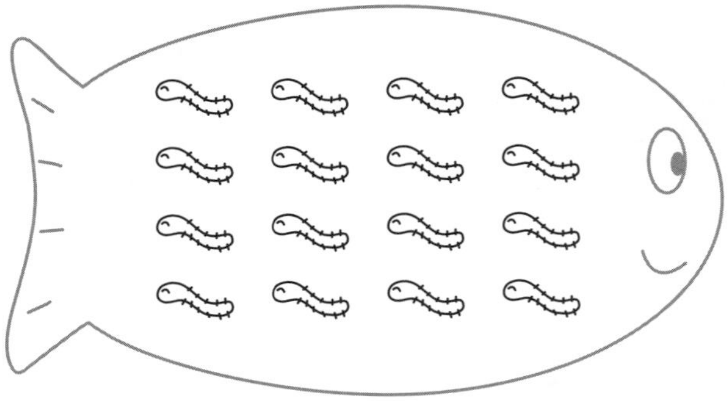

Divide the worms into 8 equal parts and colour 3 parts.

Three _____ of the worms are coloured.

⑮

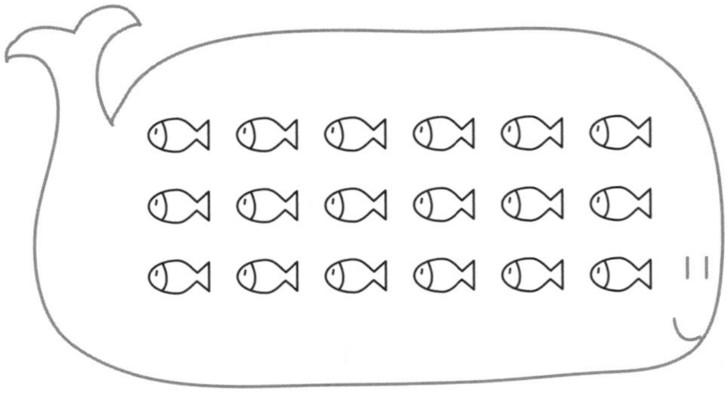

Divide the fish into 6 equal parts and colour 2 parts.

_____ _____ of the fish are coloured.

⑯

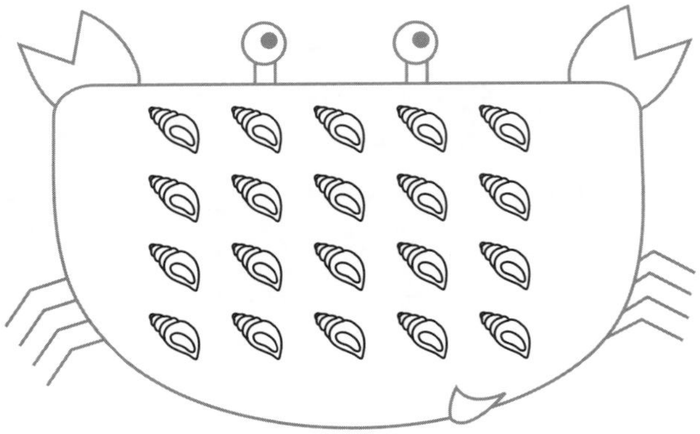

Divide the shells into 5 equal parts and colour 4 parts.

_____ _____ of the shells are coloured.

⑰

Divide the stars into 3 equal parts and colour 2 parts.

_____ _____ of the stars are coloured.

ISBN: 978-1-897164-31-0

Draw lines and colour the correct number of parts of the diagrams to match the fractions. Then circle the greater fraction.

⑱ four tenths   three fifths
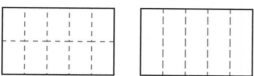

⑲ three eighths   two fourths
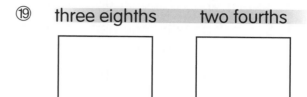

⑳ five ninths   two thirds
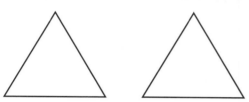

㉑ five sixths   three fifths
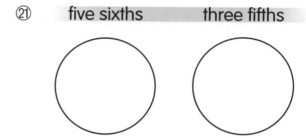

Colour the correct number of parts to match each fraction. Then put the fractions in order. Write the letters.

㉒
A two sixths
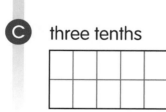

B three fifths

C three tenths
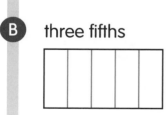

From greatest to least:

____ , ____ , ____

㉓
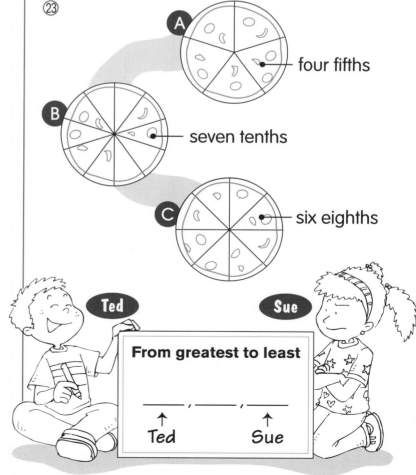

A — four fifths
B — seven tenths
C — six eighths

From greatest to least
____ , ____ , ____
↑ Ted   ↑ Sue

Each side is 48 cm.

Mr. Square
- 4 sides
- 4 vertices

18

2-D Shapes (1)

- Identify and compare polygons.
- Sort polygons by geometric property, such as number of sides and side lengths.
- Identify congruent 2-D shapes.

Colour and name the polygons. Then sort them.

① **A**

B

C

D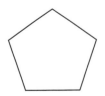

E

F

G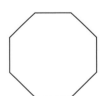

H

I

②

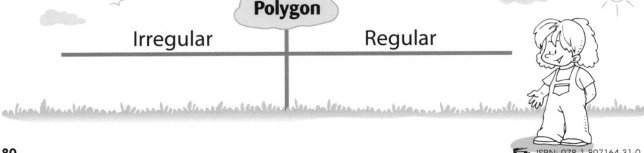

Polygon

Irregular   Regular

ISBN: 978-1-897164-31-0

Draw the missing side of each shape. Circle the vertices. Then record the number of sides and the number of vertices.

③

- _____ sides
- _____ vertices

④

- _____ sides
- _____ vertices

⑤

- _____ sides
- _____ vertices

⑥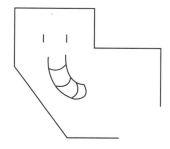

- _____ sides
- _____ vertices

⑦

- _____ sides
- _____ vertices

⑧

- _____ sides
- _____ vertices

Read each sentence. If it is correct, put a check mark ✔ in the circle; otherwise, put a cross ✗ and correct the number or word in bold to make the sentence true.

⑨ A pentagon has 5 sides and **6** vertices. ◯ ; _____

⑩ A **triangle** has 4 vertices and 4 equal sides. ◯ ; _____

⑪ An octagon has **8** sides and 8 vertices. ◯ ; _____

⑫ A hexagon has **1** side more than a pentagon. ◯ ; _____

ISBN: 978-1-897164-31-0

Two shapes are congruent when they have the same size and shape.

Congruent Shapes

e.g. Which shape is congruent to the white square?

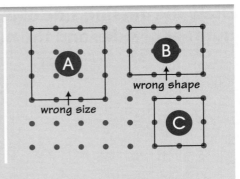

wrong shape

wrong size

C is congruent to the white square.

Put a check mark ✔ in the circle if the pair of pictures is congruent.

⑬ A   B    C

D 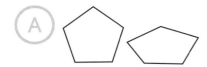   E   F

Colour the shape that is congruent to each shaded shape.

⑭ 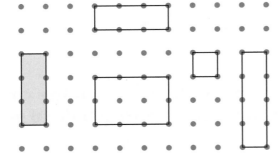   ⑮

⑯ 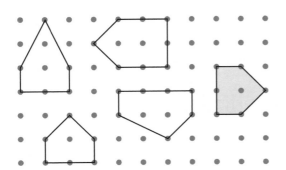   ⑰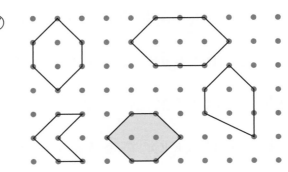

ISBN: 978-1-897164-31-0

Draw a shape that is congruent to each given figure.

⑱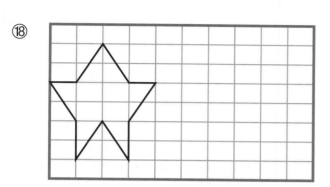

⑲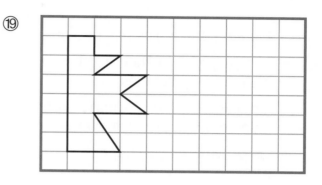

Sort the polygons by their side lengths. Write the letters.

⑳

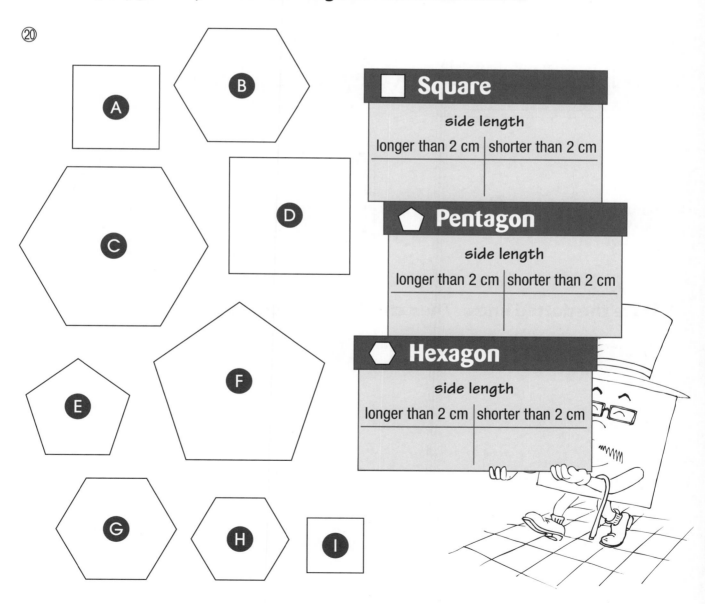

⬜ **Square**	
side length	
longer than 2 cm	shorter than 2 cm

⬠ **Pentagon**	
side length	
longer than 2 cm	shorter than 2 cm

⬡ **Hexagon**	
side length	
longer than 2 cm	shorter than 2 cm

ISBN: 978-1-897164-31-0

2-D Shapes (2)

- Identify right angles and describe angles.
- Sort polygons by their number of interior angles or right angles.
- Understand the relationship between different types of quadrilaterals.
- Draw symmetrical shapes.

Wow! Your mouth is greater than a right angle!

Colour the things that have right angles.

①

 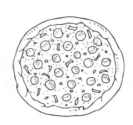 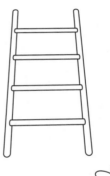

 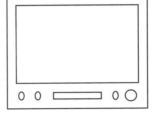 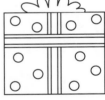

Trace the dotted lines. Then check ✔ the right angles.

② A   B   C

D   E   F

       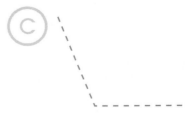

ISBN: 978-1-897164-31-0

Use the given words to describe the given angles. Then draw another angle for each type.

greater than a right angle	a right angle	smaller than a right angle

③

④

⑤

⑥

Mark the interior angles. Then colour them as specified.

greater than a right angle : **red**

a right angle : **yellow**

smaller than a right angle : **blue**

⑦

⑧

⑨

⑩

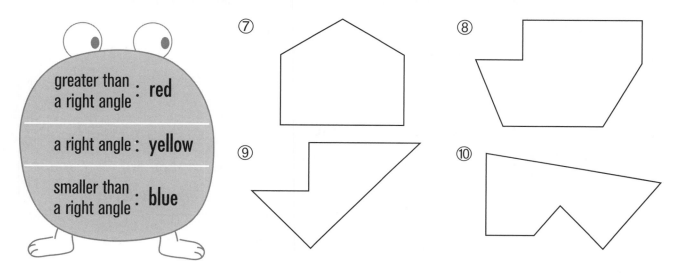

ISBN: 978-1-897164-31-0

19

ISBN: 978-1-897164-31-0

Quadrilateral:
• a polygon with 4 sides
e.g.

Rectangle: a quadrilateral in which opposite sides are equal, and all interior angles are right angles

Parallelogram: a quadrilateral whose opposite sides are parallel

Look at the interior angles of each quadrilateral. Colour them if they are right angles.

⑪

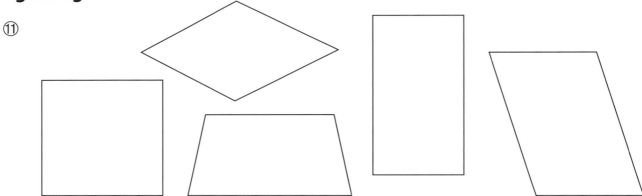

Look at each pair of quadrilaterals. Fill in the blanks and circle the correct answer.

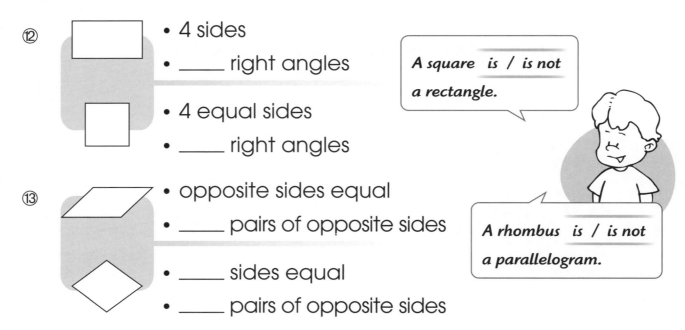

⑫
• 4 sides
• ____ right angles

• 4 equal sides
• ____ right angles

A square is / is not a rectangle.

⑬
• opposite sides equal
• ____ pairs of opposite sides

• ____ sides equal
• ____ pairs of opposite sides

A rhombus is / is not a parallelogram.

Check ✔ the picture if the dotted line is the line of symmetry of each design.

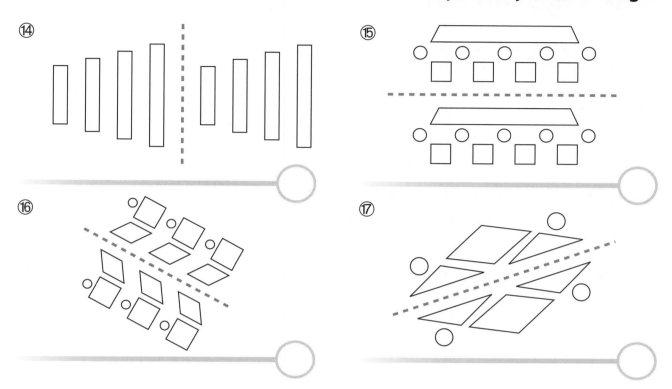

⑭   ⑮

⑯   ⑰

Draw the missing parts of each symmetrical picture.

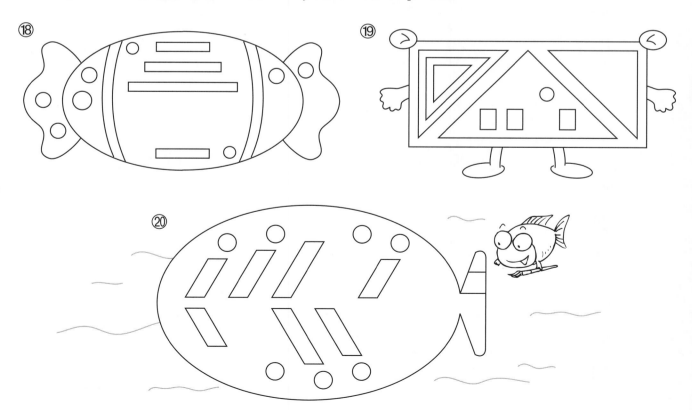

⑱   ⑲

⑳

ISBN: 978-1-897164-31-0

20

3-D Figures (1)

- Describe and name prisms and pyramids by the shape of their base.
- Sort prisms and pyramids by the number of faces, edges, or vertices.

It is a triangular prism.

Colour the bases of each prism. Then name the shape of the bases and the prism.

①
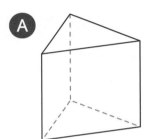
A

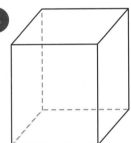
B

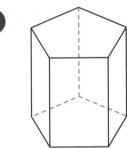
C

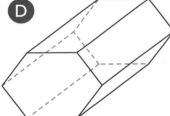
D

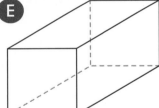
E

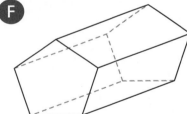
F

	Shape of Bases	Name of Prism
A		
B		
C		
D		
E		
F		

88

ISBN: 978-1-897164-31-0

Colour the base of each pyramid. Then name the shape of the base and the pyramid.

②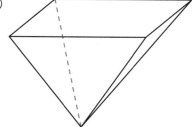

Base: _____

③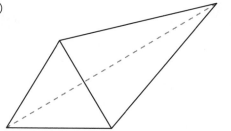

Base: _____

④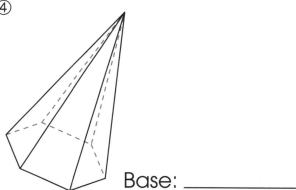

Base: _____

⑤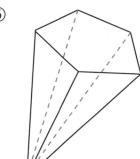

Base: _____

⑥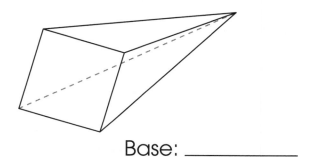

Base: _____

⑦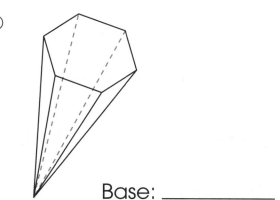

Base: _____

ISBN: 978-1-897164-31-0

Draw the missing edges and circle the vertices of each prism or pyramid. Count and write the numbers. Then sort the solids. Write the letters.

⑧ **A**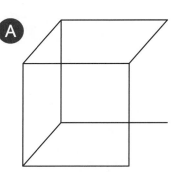

_____ faces

_____ edges

_____ vertices

B

_____ faces

_____ edges

_____ vertices

C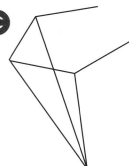

_____ faces

_____ edges

_____ vertices

D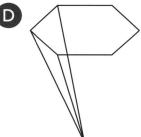

_____ faces

_____ edges

_____ vertices

E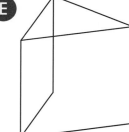

_____ faces

_____ edges

_____ vertices

F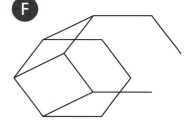

_____ faces

_____ edges

_____ vertices

⑨ **Faces**

fewer than 5: _____

5 or more: _____

⑩ **Edges**

fewer than 12: _____

12 or more: _____

⑪ **Vertices**

fewer than 6: _____

6 or more: _____

ISBN: 978-1-897164-31-0

Name the solid that can be built by the given sticks and marshmallows in each group.

⑫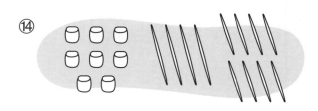

_____

⑬

_____

⑭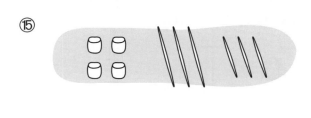

_____

⑮

_____

Check ✔ the correct answers.

⑯ Which solid has more than 6 faces?

A triangular prism   B square-based pyramid

C rectangular prism   D hexagonal pyramid

⑰ Which solid has more than 14 edges?

A hexagonal pyramid   B triangular prism

C pentagonal prism   D rectangular prism

⑱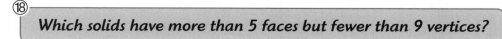

Which solids have more than 5 faces but fewer than 9 vertices?

A   B   C

ISBN: 978-1-897164-31-0

3-D Figures (2)

- Construct rectangular prisms and describe geometric properties of the prisms.
- Identify and describe the 2-D shapes that can be found in a 3-D figure.

This is Rectangular Prism.

Hi.

Colour the net that can form a rectangular prism.

① **A**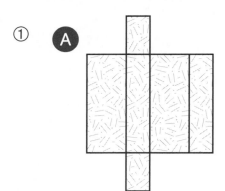

B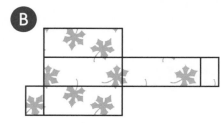

C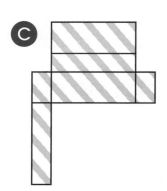

D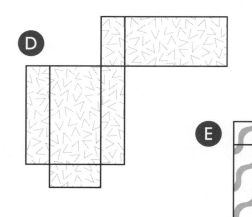

E

F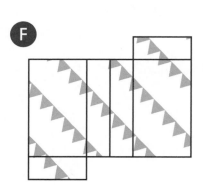

G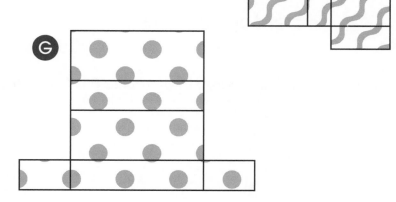

ISBN: 978-1-897164-31-0

Draw the missing parts of each net of a rectangular prism. Then match each net with the rectangular prism. Write the letter.

②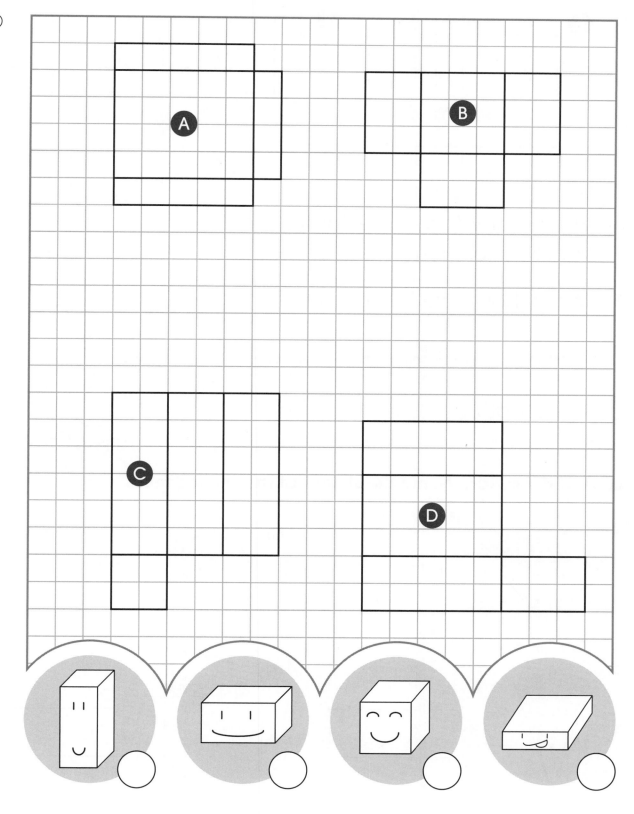

Colour each pair of congruent faces with the same colour in each net. Then answer the questions.

③ **A** 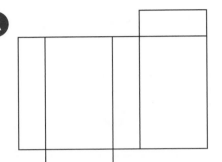   **B**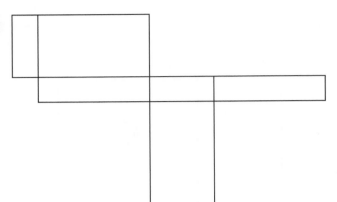

④ How many faces are there in a
rectangular prism? _____ faces

⑤ What shape are the faces? _____

⑥

How many pairs of congruent faces are there?

_____ pairs

Look at the solids. Name the shapes of the shaded faces.

⑦ 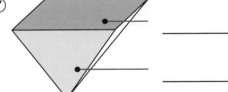 _____

_____

⑧ _____

_____

⑨ _____

_____

⑩ _____

_____

   ISBN: 978-1-897164-31-0

Colour all the faces of each solid that you can see. Then write the name of the solid and the numbers.

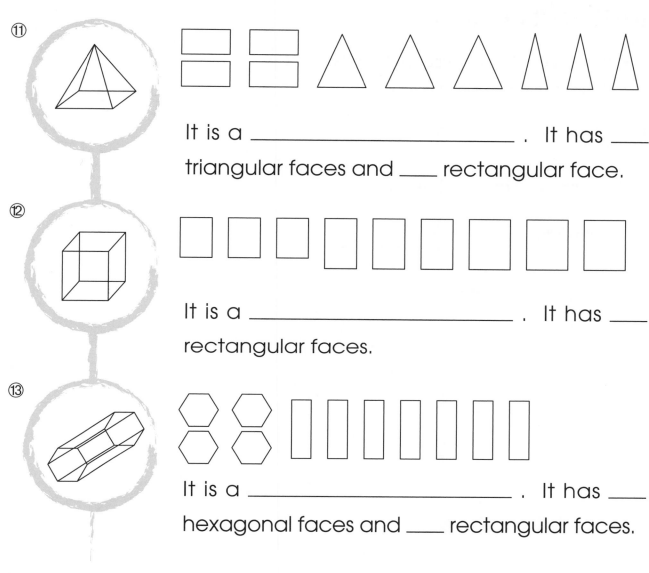

⑪ It is a _____ . It has ___ triangular faces and ___ rectangular face.

⑫ It is a _____ . It has ___ rectangular faces.

⑬ It is a _____ . It has ___ hexagonal faces and ___ rectangular faces.

Look at the solids. Answer the questions. Write the letters.

⑭ Which solids have triangular faces?

_____

⑮ Which solids have rectangular faces?

_____

ISBN: 978-1-897164-31-0

Locations of Shapes and Objects

- Describe locations of shapes and objects.
- Describe movement from one location to another.

If you go 2 squares to the right and 3 squares up, you will get me.

Look at the picture. Fill in the blanks.

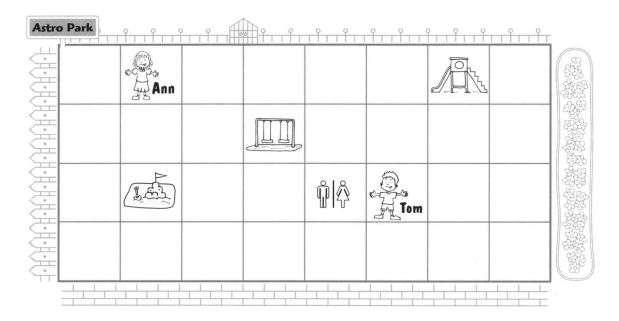

Astro Park

① The swings are _____ squares to the left of the flower bed.

② The slide is _____ squares up from the wall.

③ The washroom is _____ squares to the right of the fence.

④ The sandbox is _____ squares down from the gate.

⑤ Tom is _____ squares to the right of the sandbox and _____ squares to the left of the flower bed.

⑥ Ann is _____ squares to the right of the fence and _____ squares to the left sof the slide.

ISBN: 978-1-897164-31-0

Mark or colour the squares in the diagram to locate the children. Then answer the question.

⑦ • Sally is 5 squares to the left of the river. Colour the squares that are the possible locations of Sally yellow.

 • Sally is 3 squares up from the buildings. Put stripes on the squares that are the possible locations of Sally.

⑧ Write "Sally" in the square to show the exact location of Sally.

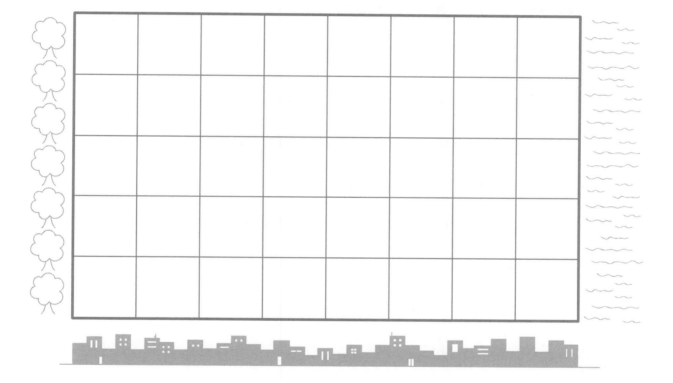

⑨ Jerry is 4 squares to the right of the trees and 5 squares up from the buildings. Write "Jerry" in the square to show the exact location of him.

⑩ How many squares are Jerry and I apart?

_____ square(s)

Sally

ISBN: 978-1-897164-31-0

Movements of objects:

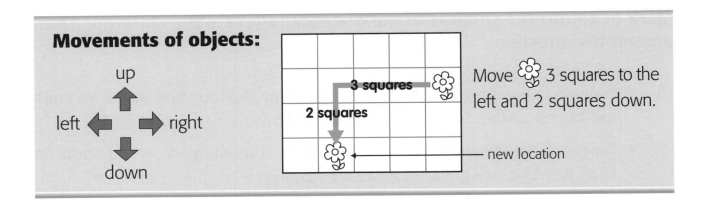

Move 🌸 3 squares to the left and 2 squares down.

Draw lines to show the movements of the objects. Then draw the objects in the squares to show the new locations.

⑪ Move

- 🍭 3 squares to the right and 1 square down.

- 🌳 2 squares to the left and 4 squares down.

- ⭐ 3 squares to the left and 3 squares up.

- 🏠 4 squares to the right and 1 square up.

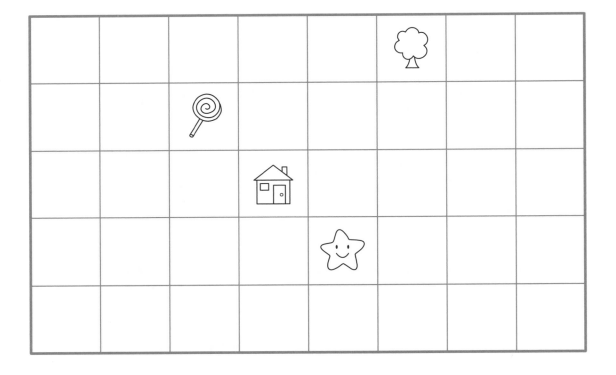

  ISBN: 978-1-897164-31-0

Look at the diagram. Help each person find the shortest path to go to the destination. Then answer the questions.

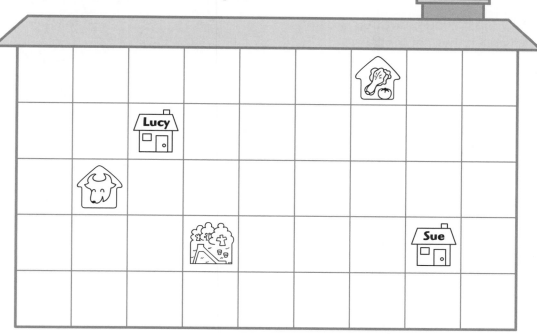

⑫ Sue wants to visit Lucy. Draw lines to show her path and describe it.

_____

⑬ Lucy's mom wants to go to the grocery store. Draw lines to show her path and describe it.

_____

⑭ *I am in the park. If I want to go to the steak house, how should I go? Draw lines and describe it.*

Mary

_____

⑮ *We are in the park. We want to go to Sue's house. Draw lines to show our path and describe it.*

_____

ISBN: 978-1-897164-31-0

Transformations

- Identify flips, slides, and turns using objects and physical motions.

I'm sliding.

See which pairs of pictures show slides. Check ✔ the letters.

①
Before **After**

Ⓐ

Before **After**

Ⓑ

Before **After**

Ⓒ

Before **After**

Ⓓ

Follow the arrow to draw the slide image of each picture.

②

③

④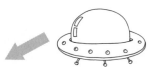

⑤

ISBN: 978-1-897164-31-0

Which is the flip image of the picture on the left?   Colour it.

Draw the missing parts of each flip image.

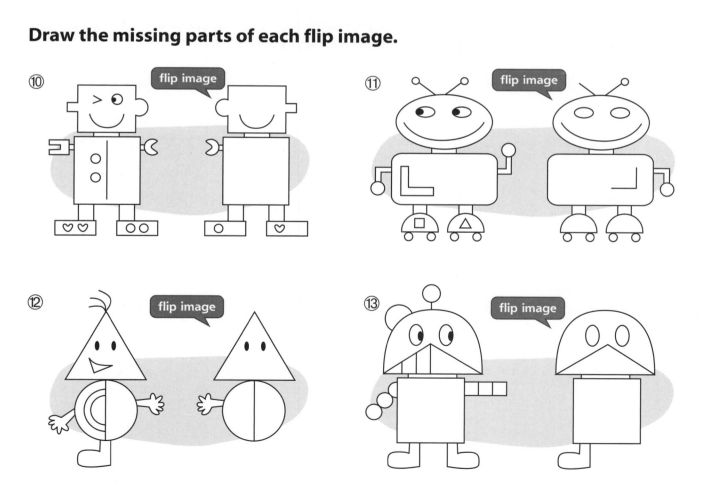

ISBN: 978-1-897164-31-0

For each picture, which are the turn images?   Check ✔ the letters.

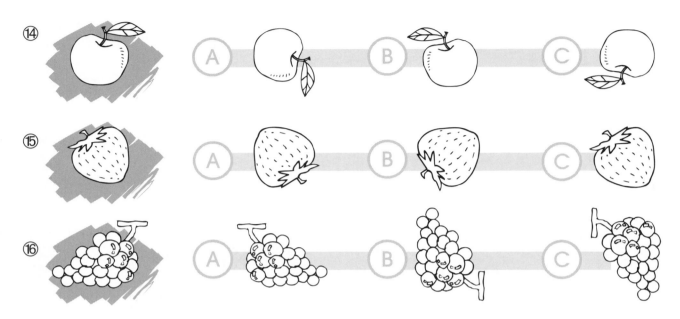

Trace each shape with tracing paper and cut it.   Then draw the missing sides of its turn image with the help of the cutout.

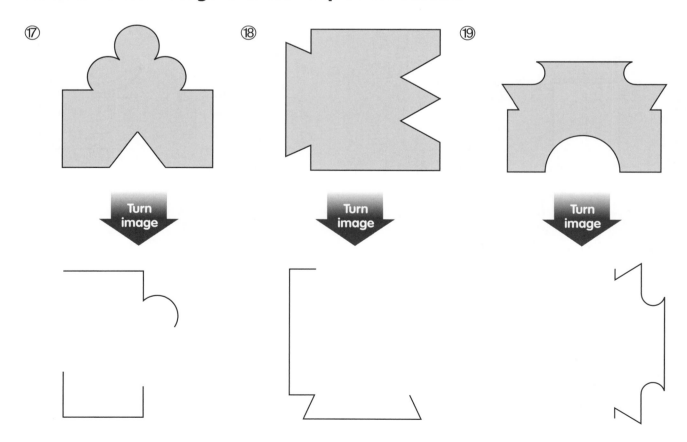

ISBN: 978-1-897164-31-0

We can use our hands to show the motion of "slide", "flip", and "turn".

Slide **Flip** **Turn**

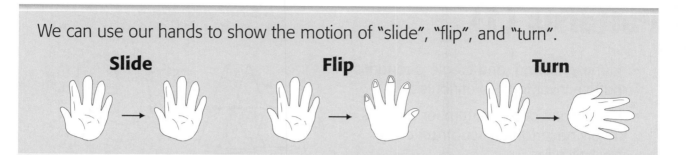

For each picture, tell whether the motion is a slide, flip, or turn.

⑳

㉑

㉒

_____   _____   _____

Tell whether each image is a slide image, a flip image, or a turn image of each picture.

㉓

㉔

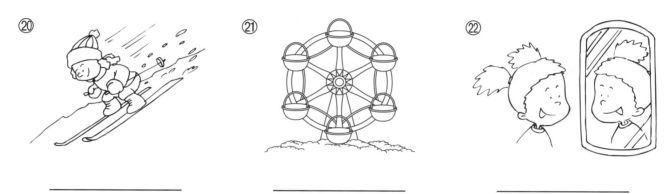

_____   _____

㉕

㉖

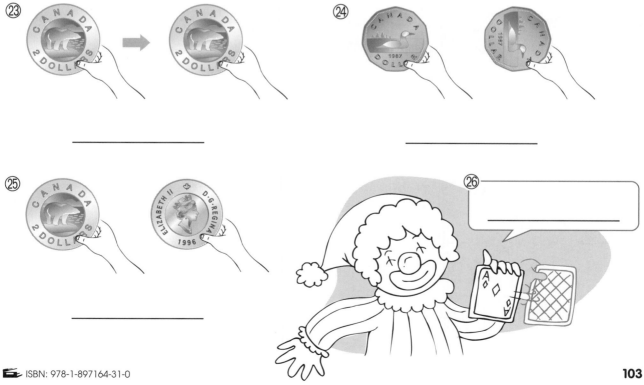

_____

ISBN: 978-1-897164-31-0

Patterns (1)

- Identify, extend, and create a repeating pattern involving two attributes.
- Identify and describe number patterns involving addition, subtraction, or multiplication.
- Describe and extend growing or shrinking patterns.

I can use cards to show a shrinking pattern.

Colour the shapes as specified. Then draw and colour the next two shapes for each pattern.

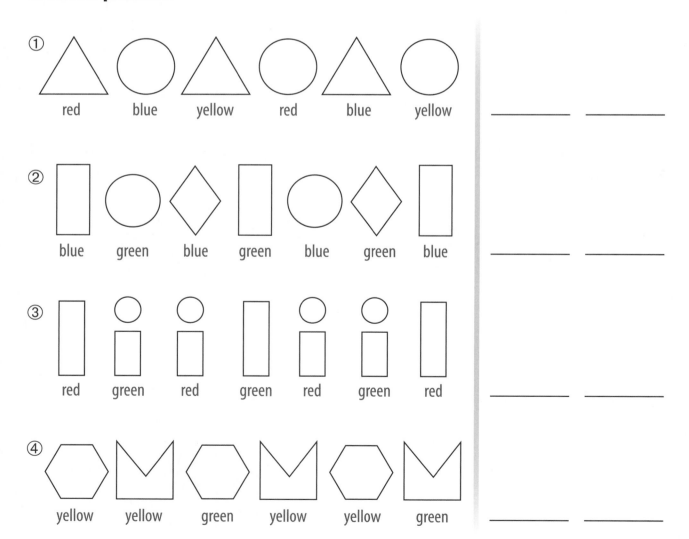

① red   blue   yellow   red   blue   yellow   ____ ____

② blue   green   blue   green   blue   green   blue   ____ ____

③ red   green   red   green   red   green   red   ____ ____

④ yellow   yellow   green   yellow   yellow   green   ____ ____

ISBN: 978-1-897164-31-0

Colour the pictures as specified. Follow the pattern in each group to draw and colour the next picture. Then fill in the blanks and circle the correct word to complete what the animal says.

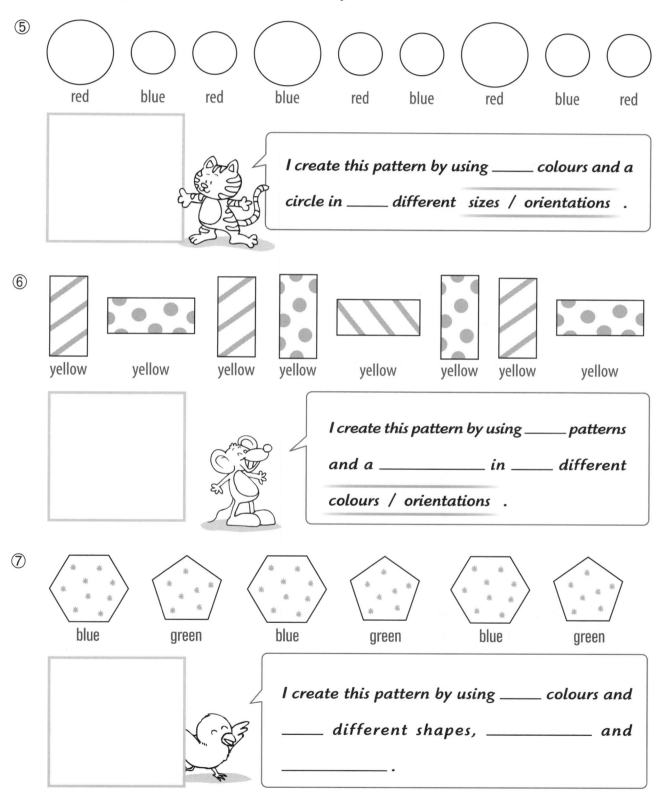

⑤

red   blue   red   blue   red   blue   red   blue   red

I create this pattern by using _____ colours and a

circle in _____ different sizes / orientations .

⑥

yellow   yellow   yellow   yellow   yellow   yellow   yellow   yellow

I create this pattern by using _____ patterns

and a _____ in _____ different

colours / orientations .

⑦

blue   green   blue   green   blue   green

I create this pattern by using _____ colours and

_____ different shapes, _____ and

_____ .

ISBN: 978-1-897164-31-0

Find the pattern in each group. Draw the missing pictures. Then write "growing" or "shrinking" on the lines.

⑧ a.

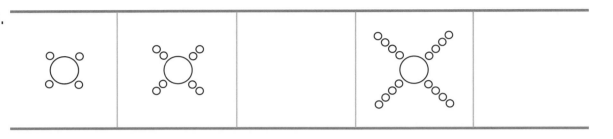

b. It is a _____ pattern.

⑨ a.

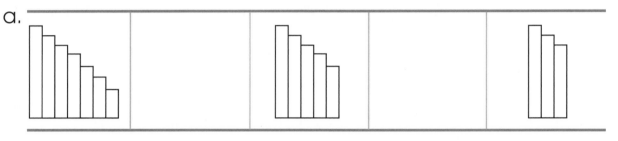

b. It is a _____ pattern.

⑩ a.

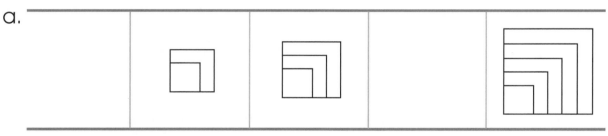

b. It is a _____ pattern.

Follow each pattern to find the next two numbers. Then tell whether each pattern is growing or shrinking.

⑪ 5   10   15   20   25   _____   _____   a _____ pattern

⑫ 30   27   24   21   18   _____   _____   a _____ pattern

⑬ 100   90   80   70   60   _____   _____   a _____ pattern

ISBN: 978-1-897164-31-0

Multiple:

the product of a given whole number multiplied by any other whole number

e.g. Multiples of 4: **4**, **8**, **12**, ...
↑   ↑   ↑
1 x 4 2 x 4 3 x 4

Colour, mark, or circle the numbers on the hundreds chart. Then circle the correct answers.

1	2	3	4	5	6	7	8	9	10
11	12	13	14	15	16	17	18	19	20
21	22	23	24	25	26	27	28	29	30
31	32	33	34	35	36	37	38	39	40
41	42	43	44	45	46	47	48	49	50
51	52	53	54	55	56	57	58	59	60
61	62	63	64	65	66	67	68	69	70
71	72	73	74	75	76	77	78	79	80
81	82	83	84	85	86	87	88	89	90
91	92	93	94	95	96	97	98	99	100

⑭ Colour the multiples of 9 yellow and circle the multiples of 5.

⑮ The multiples of 9 run   in rows / in columns / diagonally   .

⑯ The multiples of 5 run   in rows / in columns / diagonally   .

⑰ Put a "**/**" on the multiples of 3.

⑱ *Are all the multiples of 9 also the multiples of 3?*

Patterns (2)

- Create a number pattern involving addition or subtraction.
- Use number sequences to represent simple geometric patterns.
- Determine the missing numbers in equations.

$25 + 9 = 30 +$ ■

The answer is 4.

Follow the pattern rule to create a number pattern starting with the given number.

① Adding 7 each time

0 ___ ___ ___ ___ ___ ___ ___

② Subtracting 3 each time

42 ___ ___ ___ ___ ___ ___ ___

③ Adding 4 each time

20 ___ ___ ___ ___ ___ ___ ___

④ Subtracting 5 each time

40 ___ ___ ___ ___ ___ ___ ___

⑤ *Make a number pattern that starts at 24 and extends by adding 6 each time.*

___ ___ ___ ___ ___ ___

⑥ *Make a number pattern that starts at 80 and extends by subtracting 8 each time.*

___ ___ ___ ___ ___ ___

ISBN: 978-1-897164-31-0

Follow each pattern to draw the next picture. Use a number sequence to represent the number of sticks used to make each figure. Then answer the question.

⑦ a.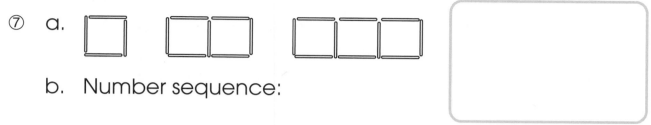

   b. Number sequence:

   _____ , _____ , _____ , _____

   c. How many sticks are there in the 6th figure?

   _____ sticks

⑧ a.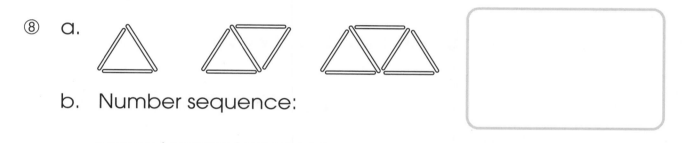

   b. Number sequence:

   _____ , _____ , _____ , _____

   c. How many sticks are there in the 6th figure?

   _____ sticks

⑨ a.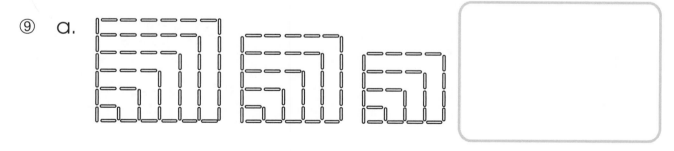

   b. Number sequence:

   _____ , _____ , _____ , _____

   c. *How many sticks are there in the 5th figure?*

   _____ sticks

ISBN: 978-1-897164-31-0

Look at each number sentence. Find the missing number.

⑩ 10 – 3   = 7

3 +  = 10

⑪ 4   + 20   = 24

24 – ⬭ = 4

⑫ 15 – 8   = 7

7 + ⬭ = 15

⑬ 6   + 13   = 19

⬭ – 6   = 13

⑭ 9 + 16   = 25

25 – ⬭ = 16

⑮ 30   – 18   = 12

⬭ + 18   = 30

Find the missing numbers with the help of the given equations.

23 + 7 = 30   4 + 12 = 16   7 + 9 = 16

21 + 4 = 25   8 + 9 = 17

23 – 16 = 7

32 – 5 = 27   21 – 18 = 3

3 + 15 = 18   9 + 3 = 12

41 – 16 = 25   20 – 6 = 14

⑯ 16 – _____ = 9

⑰ 25 – _____ = 4

⑱ 7 + _____ = 23

⑲ _____ + 16 = 41

⑳ 18 – _____ = 15

㉑ _____ – 3 = 9

㉒ 3 + _____ = 21

㉓ 27 + _____ = 32

㉔ _____ + 14 = 20

㉕ _____ – 7 = 23

㉖ _____ – 9 = 8

㉗ 16 – _____ = 12

ISBN: 978-1-897164-31-0

Steps to solve equations:

1st Simplify the equation.

2nd Use guess-and-test method to find the solution.

e.g. $26 + 5 = 40 - \heartsuit$ ← Find the sum first.

$31 = 40 - \heartsuit$ ← Think: What number should be subtracted?

$\heartsuit = 9$ ← $40 - 9 = 31$

Simplify the equations. Then solve them.

㉘ $\heartsuit + 4 = 16 - 7$

㉙ $\star - 4 = 18 + 1$

㉚ $12 + 3 = 21 - ☀$

㉛ $☾ - 6 = 15 + 8$

㉜ $15 + 2 = 27 - 🍎$

㉝ $18 - 3 = 10 + ◯$

㉞

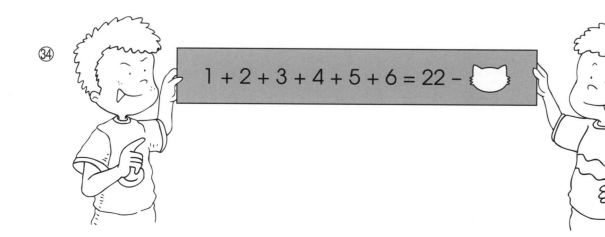

$1 + 2 + 3 + 4 + 5 + 6 = 22 - 🐱$

ISBN: 978-1-897164-31-0

Graphs (1)

- Read and describe data presented in pictographs using many-to-one correspondence.
- Make pictographs to display data with appropriate titles and labels.

George, you have got the highest score, 550 marks.

See how many ice cream cones Mr. Winter sold yesterday. Look at the pictograph. Answer the questions.

Number of Ice Cream Cones Sold Yesterday

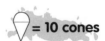 = 10 cones

Flavour	
Strawberry	
Vanilla	
Chocolate	
Neapolitan	

① How many flavours were there?   _____ flavours

② How many vanilla ice cream cones were sold?   _____ cones

③ How many Neapolitan ice cream cones were sold?   _____ cones

④ How many more strawberry ice cream cones were sold than chocolate ice cream cones?   _____ more

⑤ If each ice cream cone cost $2, how much did Mr. Winter get from selling the ice cream cones yesterday? $ _____

ISBN: 978-1-897164-31-0

Uncle Tim recorded the number of each kind of toys left in his toy shop this week. Look at the pictograph. Answer the questions.

Toys in Uncle Tim's Shop ☐ = 20 items

⑥ How many 🚗 are there? _____

⑦ How many 🐸 are there? _____

⑧ How many toy cars are there in all? _____ toy cars

⑨ How many wind-up toys are there in all? _____ wind-up toys

⑩ If the number of each kind of toys were the same at the beginning, which toy had the greatest sale? Explain.

_____

⑪ If Uncle Tim wants to promote one of the toys next week, which toy should it be? Give a reason.

_____

ISBN: 978-1-897164-31-0

Judy has a collection of buttons. Help her put them into four categories and use tally marks to complete the table.

I have 2 kinds of buttons, flower and square. They have either 4 holes or 2 holes.

⑫

Number			

ISBN: 978-1-897164-31-0

Look at the table on P. 114. Complete the pictograph to show the data. Then answer the questions.

⑬

Each picture represents 4 buttons.

⑭ How many flower buttons does Judy have in all?

_____ flower buttons

⑮ How many buttons does she have in all?

_____ buttons

⑯

If I give 37 buttons to my grandma, how many buttons will I have left?

_____ buttons

 ISBN: 978-1-897164-31-0

Graphs (2)

The mode size of the T-shirt is medium.

- Read and describe data presented in a vertical or horizontal bar graph.
- Complete or make bar graphs to show the data.
- Understand and identify the mode in a set of data.

Sales of T-shirts

Read the bar graph showing the favourite insects of Mrs. Moxam's class. Then answer the questions.

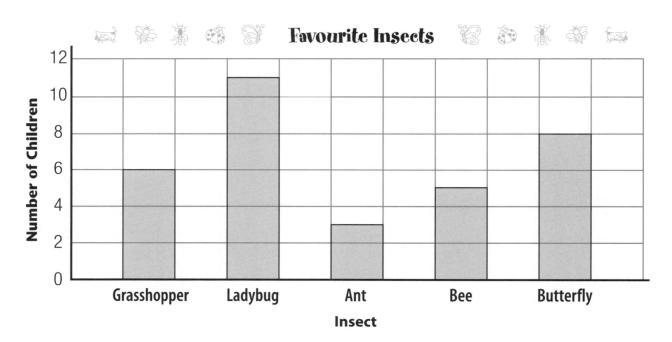

① How many children like the butterfly? _____ children

② How many children like the bee? _____ children

③ Which insect is the most popular? _____

④ Which insect is the least popular? _____

⑤ How many children are there in Mrs. Moxam's class? _____ children

ISBN: 978-1-897164-31-0

Uncle Sam has 5 grocery stores. See how long it took each store to sell 10 cartons of juice. Complete the vertical bar graph to show the data and answer the questions.

Store	A	B	C	D	E
Number of Days	30	25	15	20	10

⑥

Days Taken to Sell 10 Cartons of Juice

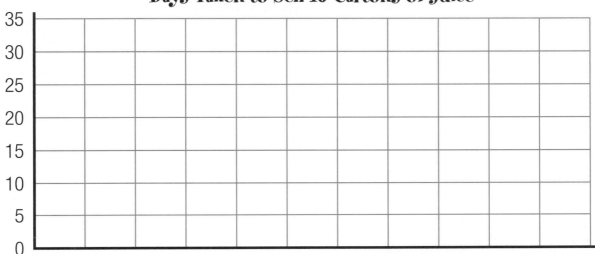

⑦ What is the title of the graph?

_____

⑧ How many days does each square represent? _____ days

⑨ Which stores took more than 3 weeks to sell 10 cartons of juice? _____

⑩ Which store had the best sales? How many cartons of juice did it sell each day on average? _____ ; _____ carton(s)

ISBN: 978-1-897164-31-0

Judy is preparing muffins for her school's fundraising program tomorrow. Look at the table. Help her complete the horizontal bar graph to show the data. Then answer the questions.

Flavour	Carrot	Oatmeal	Raisin	Blueberry	Banana
Number	22	19	11	13	18

⑪ **Judy's Muffins**

Carrot

0 2 4 6 8 10 12 14 16 18 20 22 24

⑫ How many different flavours are there? _____ flavours

⑬ How many muffins are with fruit? _____ muffins

⑭ How many muffins has she made in all? _____ muffins

⑮ If each muffin costs $1, how much will be collected from selling all the muffins? $ _____

ISBN: 978-1-897164-31-0

Mode: the value that occurs most often in a set of data

e.g. Ted's 7-day savings: 32¢, 16¢, 32¢, 18¢, 40¢, 32¢, 15¢

Since 32¢ occurs most often, the mode savings is 32¢.

Look at each set of data. Find the mode.

⑯ The heights of 12 students:

120 cm	108 cm	98 cm	120 cm
108 cm	96 cm	114 cm	125 cm
108 cm	109 cm	105 cm	111 cm

The mode height is _____ .

⑰ The weights of 15 women:

62 kg	58 kg	63 kg	70 kg	58 kg
63 kg	59 kg	58 kg	62 kg	62 kg
58 kg	61 kg	53 kg	57 kg	70 kg

Mode weight: _____

⑱ The lengths of 18 ropes:

46 cm	70 cm	52 cm	63 cm	60 cm
70 cm	54 cm	62 cm	70 cm	48 cm
49 cm	61 cm	70 cm	62 cm	70 cm
52 cm	70 cm	70 cm		

Mode length: _____

⑲ The costs of 10 rings:

$275	$316	$127	$316	$275
$117	$98	$275	$400	$400

The mode cost is _____ .

ISBN: 978-1-897164-31-0

Probability

- Predict the frequency of an outcome in a simple probability experiment.
- Understand the fairness in a game and relate this to the occurrence of equally likely outcomes.

If I spin 6 times, I predict that the pointer will land on an animal 3 times and a plant 3 times.

See what probability experiments the children are doing.   Check ✔ the best predictions.

① Draw a ball from the box 20 times.

Predictions

A ⊙ – 4 times
   ⊘ – 16 times

B ⊙ – 10 times
   ⊘ – 10 times

C ⊙ – 15 times
   ⊘ – 5 times

D ⊙ – 0 times
   ⊘ – 20 times

② Pick a card from the bag 50 times.

Predictions

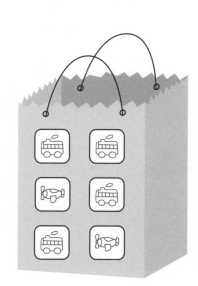

A 🚒 – 40 times
   ✈ – 10 times

B 🚢 – 34 times
   ✈ – 16 times

C 🚒 – 34 times
   ✈ – 16 times

D 🚒 – 16 times
   ✈ – 34 times

ISBN: 978-1-897164-31-0

Look at the things that the children have. Answer the questions. Then predict the results.

③ Draw a card from Elaine's collection.

Elaine's Collection

    a. What are the possible outcomes?

    _____

    b. Are the chances of drawing a  or a  the same?

    _____

④ If Elaine draws a card 50 times without looking, what results do you predict?

Prediction: _____ times _____ times _____ times

⑤ Spin the spinner once. What things may the pointer land on?

_____

⑥ If Joe spins the spinner 40 times, what results do you predict?

Prediction:

 _____ times _____ times

_____ times _____ times

ISBN: 978-1-897164-31-0

If a spinner is divided into equal parts and nothing on the spinner appears more than once, it is a fair spinner.

So this is a fair spinner.

Check ✔ the fair spinners.

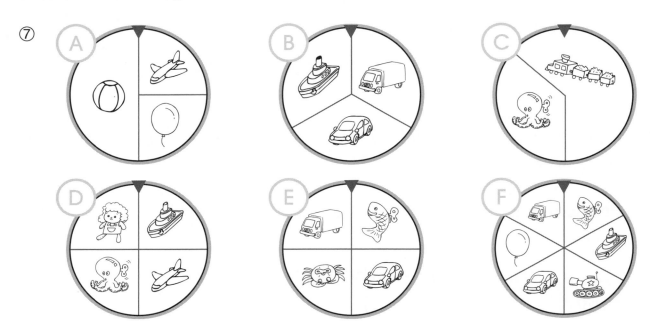

⑦ A B C

D E F

Draw lines on each spinner and colour it.

⑧ A 4-colour fair spinner

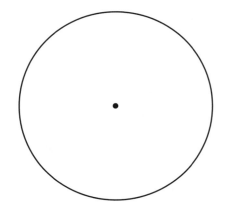

⑨ A 6-colour fair spinner

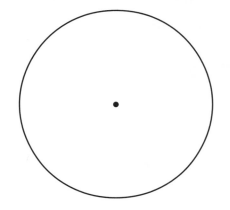

ISBN: 978-1-897164-31-0

The children are going to draw a marble from the bag. Help them answer the questions.

⑩

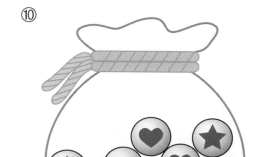

a. If Judy draws a marble, is it more likely to get a star marble?

_____

b. Is it equally likely to get a star or a heart marble? If not, take out the fewest marbles in the bag to make the game fair.

_____

⑪

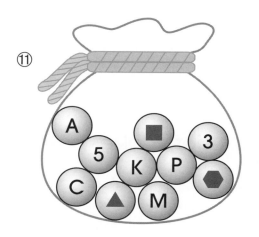

a. If Katie draws a marble, is it more likely to get a letter marble?

_____

b. Cross out ✗ the fewest marbles in the bag to make the game fair.

Colour the spinner to match what Annie says.

⑫

It is a 4–colour spinner. I spun it 100 times. Here is the result.

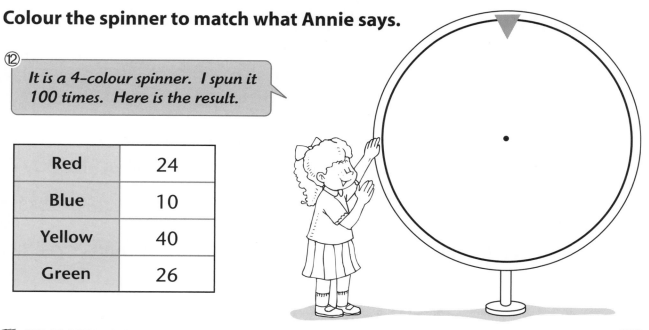

Red	24
Blue	10
Yellow	40
Green	26

ISBN: 978-1-897164-31-0

Do the divisions with the help of the given pictures.

①

a.

$$4 \overline{)\ 20}$$

b.

$$6 \overline{)\ 20} \quad R\ \underline{\quad}$$

②

a.

$$3 \overline{)\ 15}$$

b.

$$4 \overline{)\ 15} \quad R\ \underline{\quad}$$

Find the answers.

③

$5

28 pieces

a. How much do 8 boxes of cookies cost?

_____ = _____ $ _____

b. If Raymond puts a box of cookies equally into 5 groups, how many cookies are there in each group?

_____ = _____   _____ cookies

④

Special

$3

a. Mrs. Winter needs 48 muffins. How many packs of muffins does she need to buy?

_____ = _____   _____ packs

b. How much do 9 packs of muffins cost?

_____ = _____ $ _____

ISBN: 978-1-897164-31-0

Name the shapes. Draw lines to divide the shapes into equal parts. Then colour the parts and fill in the blanks with fractional names.

⑤   a.

b.   Divide the shapes into 5 equal parts and colour 3 parts.

c.   _____ of the shapes are coloured.

⑥   a.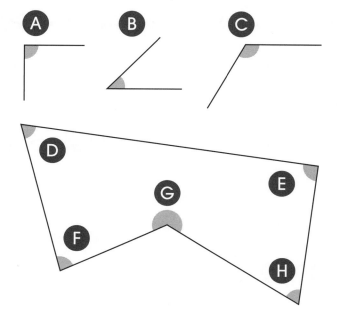

b.   Divide the shapes into 4 equal parts and colour 3 parts.

c.   _____ of the shapes are coloured.

Sort the angles. Write the letters.

⑦

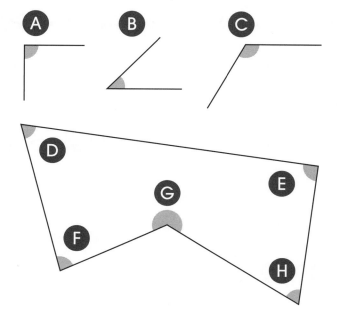

• greater than a right angle

_____

• a right angle

_____

• smaller than a right angle

_____

ISBN: 978-1-897164-31-0

Colour the base(s) of each solid. Then name the shape of the base(s) and the solid.

⑧

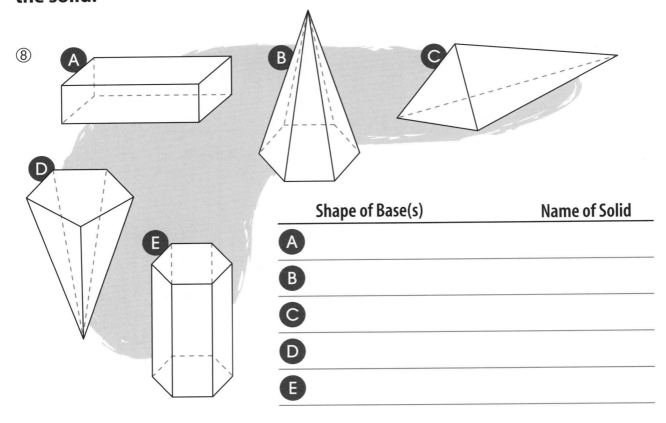

	Shape of Base(s)	Name of Solid
A		
B		
C		
D		
E		

Look at the solids above. Answer the questions.

⑨ How many faces does **A** have?   _____ faces

⑩ How many edges does **D** have?   _____ edges

⑪ Which solids have more than 7 vertices?   _____

⑫ Which solids have rectangular faces?   _____

⑬ Colour the correct number of shapes to match the faces that **B** has.

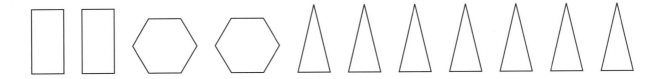

ISBN: 978-1-897164-31-0

Draw the new locations of the objects. Then help each person find the shortest path to get the object. Describe the route.

⑭ **Move**
- the chair 5 squares to the right and 2 squares up
- the tree 5 squares to the left and 3 squares down
- the doll 2 squares to the left and 3 squares up

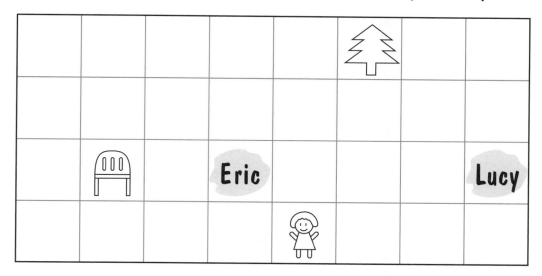

⑮ Lucy wants to get the doll in the new location. Describe the route that she should take.

_____

⑯ Eric wants to get the chair in the new location. Describe the route that he should take.

_____

Draw the missing parts of each flip image.

⑰   flip image

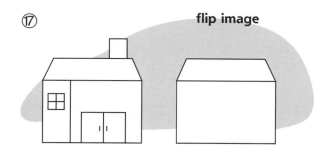

⑱   flip image

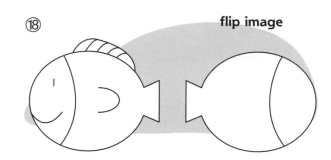

ISBN: 978-1-897164-31-0

Colour the pictures as specified. Follow the pattern in each group to draw and colour the next picture. Then fill in the blanks and circle the correct word to complete the sentence.

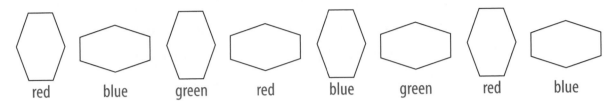

⑲

red   blue   green   red   blue   green   red   blue

a. [box]

b. This pattern is created by using ____ colours and a _____ in ____ different   patterns / orientations .

⑳

red   red   red   red   red   red   red   red   red

a. [box]

b. This pattern is created by using ____ patterns and a _____ in ____ different   sizes / colours .

Follow each number to find the next two numbers. Then tell whether each pattern is growing or shrinking.

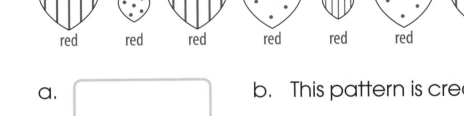

㉑   10   100   1000   10000   _____   _____

This is a _____ pattern.

㉒   444444   44444   4444   444   _____   _____

This is a _____ pattern.

ISBN: 978-1-897164-31-0

Complete the horizontal bar graph to show the data. Then answer the questions.

I sold lots of balloons yesterday.

Colour	Red	Yellow	Green	Blue
No. of Balloons Sold	18	20	15	19

㉓

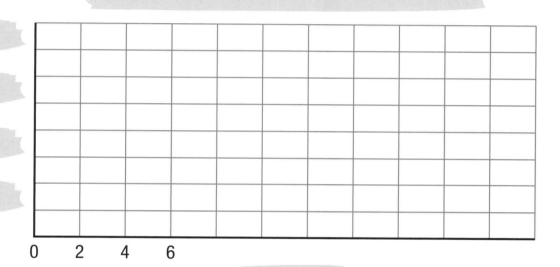

0   2   4   6

㉔ How many more red balloons than green balloons were sold?

_____ more

㉕ How many balloons were sold in all?

_____ balloons

Check ✔ the fair spinners.

㉖

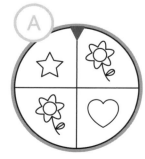

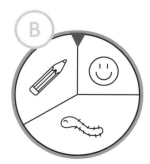

ISBN: 978-1-897164-31-0

ISBN: 978-1-897164-31-0

ISBN: 978-1-897164-31-0

Groundhog Day

February 2 is Groundhog Day in North America. Every year on this day, we wait eagerly to see if the groundhog will come out of its burrow to find its shadow.

This idea comes from an old Scottish verse:

"If Candlemas Day is bright and clear, there will be two winters in the year."

Candlemas Day is halfway between the first day of winter (December 21) and the first day of spring (March 21). Some people used to believe that if it was sunny on this day, then the rest of the winter would be cold. But if it was cloudy on this day, then the rest of the winter would be mild and short.

If the groundhog sees its shadow, there will be six more weeks of winter. If it does not see its shadow, then we know that spring will soon be with us.

Groundhogs are the only animal to have a day named after them.

ISBN: 978-1-897164-31-0

A. Match the pictures with the statements. Write the letters in the boxes.

Ⓐ The rest of the winter would be cold.

Ⓑ The rest of the winter would be mild.

Ⓒ There will be six more weeks of winter.

Ⓓ Spring will soon come.

1. **Candlemas Day**

2. **Candlemas Day**

3.

4.

B. You have a chance to name a day after an animal. Which day and what animal will you choose? Draw a picture of the animal and write the reason.

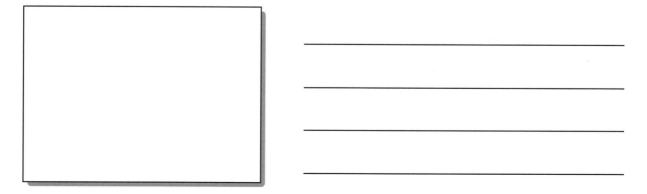

ISBN: 978-1-897164-31-0

Silent Consonants

Some consonants like "**b**", "**g**", "**gh**", "**h**", "**k**", "**l**", "**n**", "**s**", "**t**", and "**w**" are silent in some words.

Examples: bri<u>gh</u>t   <u>k</u>now   hal<u>f</u>   t<u>w</u>o

C.   Say the things. Complete the words with the correct silent consonants.

1.

___cissors

2.

sc___ool

3.

___reath

4.
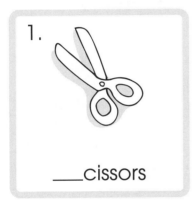
cas___le

5.

sta___k

6.
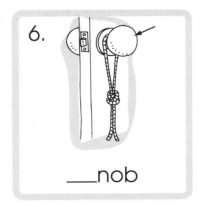
___nob

7.

com___

8.

slei___ ___

ISBN: 978-1-897164-31-0

D.   Read the sentences.   Circle all the silent consonants.

1.   The knight was frightened by the lightning last night.

2.   Don't write the answers in the wrong column.

3.   He designed eight Christmas cards.

4.   The scientist stayed calm when he saw
the ghost.

5.   The rhino is blowing a whistle
beside the lamb.

E.   Write two words with each silent consonant.

1.   **b**   _____   _____

2.   **g**   _____   _____

3.   **gh**   _____   _____

4.   **h**   _____   _____

5.   **k**   _____   _____

6.   **l**   _____   _____

7.   **n**   _____   _____

8.   **s**   _____   _____

9.   **t**   _____   _____

10. **w**   _____   _____

ISBN: 978-1-897164-31-0

The New Student

We have a new student in our class. She sits beside me. Her name is Emelyn Marquez. She comes from the Philippines. She came here with her parents. They live with her grandparents.

Emelyn came from a town called Dupax del Sur. They plant a lot of rice there. She taught us a song about planting rice. We all did gestures to go with the song. We sang the song in English. When we finished, Emelyn sang the song in her native language. It was beautiful.

Planting rice is never fun

Planting rice is never fun.
Bend from morn till the set of sun.
Cannot stand, cannot sit.
Cannot rest for a little bit.

Emelyn said she liked planting rice, but it was a lot of hard work. I asked Emelyn if she wanted to come over after school this week. Guess what! She just phoned me. Her mother said she can come over tomorrow. I think Emelyn and I will be best friends!

ISBN: 978-1-897164-31-0

A. Read the story and check ✔ the way of planting rice in the Philippines.

B. Colour Yes **for the correct sentences. Colour** No **for the wrong ones.**

1. Emelyn sits behind the writer.

Yes	No

2. Some people in the Philippines grow rice.

Yes	No

3. Dupax del Sur is a city in the Philippines.

Yes	No

4. The writer sang the song in Emelyn's native language.

Yes	No

5. Planting rice is not an easy job.

Yes	No

6. The writer likes planting rice.

Yes	No

7. The writer wants to be Emelyn's best friend.

Yes	No

ISBN: 978-1-897164-31-0

Hard and Soft "C"

The consonant "**c**" usually has a **hard sound**.

Examples: <u>c</u>ome <u>c</u>an <u>c</u>all

When "c" is followed by "e", "i", or "y", it usually has a **soft sound**.

Examples: <u>c</u>ell <u>c</u>ity <u>c</u>ycle

C. Say the things. Write the letters in the correct places.

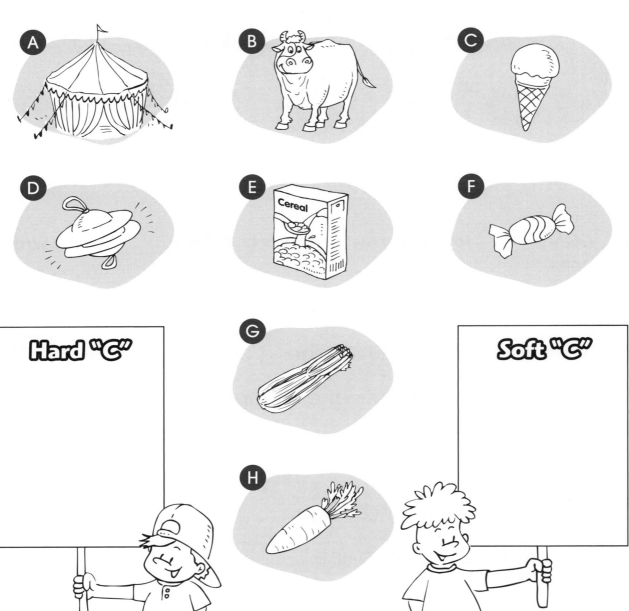

ISBN: 978-1-897164-31-0

Hard and Soft "G"

The consonant "**g**" usually has a **hard sound**.

Examples: go   guess   goat

When "g" is followed by "e", "i", or "y", it usually has a **soft sound**.

Examples: gesture   giraffe   gypsy

D.   Say the things.   Draw lines to join the pictures to the correct signs.

Hard "G"

.

Soft "G"

.

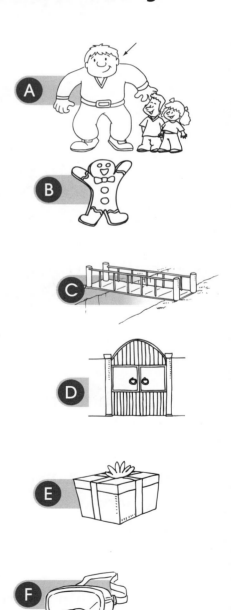

A

B

C

D

E

F

ISBN: 978-1-897164-31-0

There are many different ways to write poems. Poems don't have to rhyme. The lines of a poem can be made of many words, or only a few – or even just one! Poems can tell a story, and can fill your head with many ideas. But some poems are about an idea, and will make you think of just one thing.

Acrostic Poems

Acrostic poems are special poems. The first letter of each line spells a word. That word is like the title of the poem. Look at the two examples below.

Rain falls.
And then
I see a ribbon.
New and
Bright. Colours
Over the
Wind.

Mrs. Janet Green.
Oh, I think she is
The best.
Happy and nice
Every day.
Really, I love her a lot.

Acrostics are fun to write. Why don't you give it a try?

ISBN: 978-1-897164-31-0

A. **Write the title for each poem in the passage. Draw a picture to go with it.**

1. _____

Rain falls.
And then
I see a ribbon.
New and
Bright. Colours
Over the
Wind.

2. _____

Mrs. Janet Green.
Oh, I think she is
The best.
Happy and nice
Every day.
Really, I love her a lot.

B. **Write the acrostic poem below.**

B_____

O_____

O_____

K_____

M_____

A_____

R_____

K_____

ISBN: 978-1-897164-31-0

"Y" as a Vowel (1)

When "**y**" comes at the end of a word with no vowel or in the middle of a word with no vowel except "e" at the end, it usually sounds like a **long "i"**.

Examples: why   try   rhyme

C. Say the words. Help Felix the Fly get to the bread by colouring the words that use "y" as a vowel with the long "i" sound.

     ISBN: 978-1-897164-31-0

"Y" as a Vowel (2)

When "**y**" comes at the end of a word with another vowel in it, it usually sounds like a **long "e"**.

Examples: many   story   happy

D.   Say the words. Colour the ones that use "y" as a vowel with the long "e" sound.

1.

daisy

2.

angry

3.

monkey

4.

tray

5.
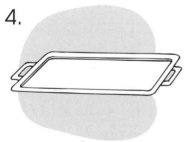
diary

6.

pyramid

7.

crystal

8.
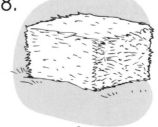
hay

9.

mummy

ISBN: 978-1-897164-31-0

What Are Things Made of?

Y ou touch something plastic every day. But have you ever wondered how we get plastic? It does not grow on trees. We do not get it from animals. So, where does plastic come from?

We know how to make things from all kinds of other things found in the world around us. For example, glass is made from sand. Clay pots and china dishes are made from clay, which comes from the soil in some places. Jewellery is made from the stones we find deep under the ground.

Where do our clothes come from? We get cotton fabric from cotton balls that grow on bushes. Leather comes from the skin of animals. We also make woollen clothes from the wool of sheep.

We eat the plants we grow and the animals we raise. We get maple syrup from the sap of maple trees. Everything we use comes from the world around us.

So...where does plastic come from? We make it from oil we find in the ground!

ISBN: 978-1-897164-31-0

A.   Match the pictures with the things they are made of. Write the letters.

(A) cotton bushes

(B) wool of sheep

(C) clay

(D) sand

(E) skin of animals

(F) oil in the ground

(G) sap of maple trees

(H) stones under the ground

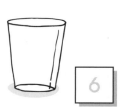

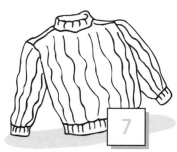

B.   Change a letter in each word below to form a word you can find in the passage.

1. g l o w   _____

2. b o i l   _____

3. t o u g h   _____

4. p l a n e s   _____

5. w o u l d   _____

6. t h i n k s   _____

ISBN: 978-1-897164-31-0

Long Vowel Digraphs

When two letters together form a long vowel sound, it is called a **long vowel digraph**.

"**Ai**", "**ay**", "**ei**", "**ea**", "**ee**", "**oa**", "**ow**", "**oo**", "**ew**", "**au**", and "**aw**" are all long vowel digraphs.

Examples: cl<u>ay</u>   sh<u>ee</u>p   gr<u>ow</u>   w<u>oo</u>l

C.   Say the words. Put them next to the correct long vowel digraphs.

tree   crew   day   jaw   eight
train   cause   load   eat   boot   know

1. ai _____

2. ay _____

3. ei _____

4. ea _____

5. ee _____

6. oa _____

7. ow _____

8. oo _____

9. ew _____

10. au _____

11. aw _____

ISBN: 978-1-897164-31-0

D. **Say the things. Cross out ✗ the ones that do not have long vowel digraphs.**

Some letters like "ea" in "leather" and "ow" in "cow" are not long vowel digraphs.

Today our gym teacher, Mr. Rollins, told us to do something special. At first, he told us to run one kilometre. Many of my classmates started to groan. They didn't want to run.

Mr. Rollins was not happy. He said that we should be glad to have a chance to exercise at school. He said that gym class is a chance to keep fit.

After we ran, Mr. Rollins told us to write about why gym class is important. He said we should be creative, so I wrote this poem.

Ode to Gym Class

Gym class is lots of fun.
We get to run and jump and play.
I think it's my favourite time of day.
And we should all be shouting "Hooray!"

I love to eat, I know it's true.
If I didn't have gym class,
I know what I'd do.
I'd get too big to fit in my shorts.
I wouldn't want to play any sports.

A Special Gym Class

I love to play what I want – what I dare.
I love to play hard, but I love to play fair.
I'd like to be voted "Most Valuable Player"!
My efforts in gym class will get me there.

ISBN: 978-1-897164-31-0

A. **Read the clues. Complete the crossword puzzle with words from the story.**

Across

A. happy
B. make a deep, sad sound
C. of great value
D. unusual
E. a kind of poem

Down

1. work out
2. best liked
3. have courage to do
4. in good health

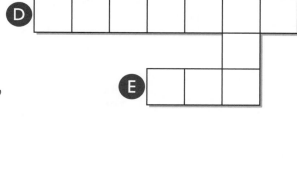

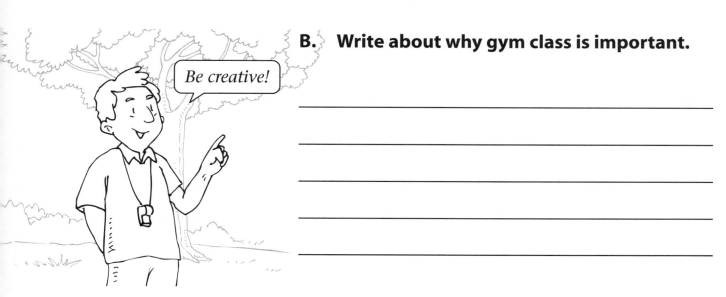

B. **Write about why gym class is important.**

Be creative!

_____

_____

_____

_____

_____

ISBN: 978-1-897164-31-0

Rhyming Words

Rhyming words are words that have the same ending sound.

Examples: fun – run   special – social

A poem may have lines ending in rhyming pairs.

C.   Say the words in each group. Cross out ✗ the one that does not rhyme with the others.

1
do
school
true
clue

2
player
hooray
day
stay

3
fair
there
dare
tail

4
sports
shorts
efforts
escorts

5
fast
grass
class
mass

6
teacher
sculpture
richer
peaches

ISBN: 978-1-897164-31-0

D. Say the things. Draw lines to match the rhyming pairs. Then write one more word that rhymes with each pair.

1.  •

2.  •

3.  •

4.  •

5.  •

6.  •

7.  •

A

B

C

D

E

F

G

 ISBN: 978-1-897164-31-0

The Frank *Slide*

Frank, Alberta was a town at the foot of Turtle Mountain, near the border of British Columbia. It was on the Canadian Pacific Railway line. The town's main business was coal mining. It was a prosperous place.

On April 29, 1903, at 4:10 a.m., something terrible happened. Turtle Mountain broke apart. It was the greatest landslide in North American history. 30 million cubic metres of limestone fell down the mountain and buried much of the town.

At that time, the population of Frank was about 600. 70 people died, but another 23 people who had been buried were rescued. This included 17 coal miners, who had been underground at the time of the slide. They rescued themselves by tunnelling upwards to safety. Three quarters of the town's homes were destroyed, and two kilometres of railway line was obliterated.

The slide lasted less than two minutes, but the debris spread over three square kilometres. Scientists have long wondered how rocks could spread so far and wide in such a short time. Many believe that, in a case like this, the rock and soil flow like a thick liquid. They believe Turtle Mountain collapsed because it was made unstable by underground coal mining and erosion by weather and water.

ISBN: 978-1-897164-31-0

A. **Check ✔ the correct sentences.**

1. Frank is a town on Turtle Mountain. ☐

2. Coal mining was Frank's main business in 1903. ☐

3. Firefighters rescued 17 coal miners underground. ☐

4. 30 million cubic metres of mud fell down the mountain in the slide. ☐

5. The Frank slide was the greatest landslide in North American history. ☐

6. Underground coal mining had made Turtle Mountain unstable. ☐

B. **Match the facts. Write the letters on the lines.**

A the population of Frank in 1903

B the day when the Frank slide took place

C the number of people rescued

D the time when the slide happened

E the duration of the slide

F the length of railway line destroyed

1. 23 ___   2. April 29, 1903 ___

3. two kilometres ___   4. 600 ___

5. two minutes ___   6. 4:10 a.m. ___

ISBN: 978-1-897164-31-0

Common and Proper Nouns

A **common noun** names any person, animal, place, or thing.

Examples: miner   deer   province   rock

A **proper noun** names a specific person, animal, place, or thing. It always begins with a capital letter.

Examples: Mr. Jenkins   Bambi   Alberta   the Olympics

C. Circle the common nouns and underline the proper nouns in the sentences.

1. Aunt Rosaline and her family moved to Edmonton last year.

2. Her daughter Sherry told me that West Edmonton Mall is the world's largest shopping centre.

3. You can find all types of shops in the mall.

4. Have you ever heard of Turtle Mountain?

5. There was a town called Frank at the foot of the mountain.

6. Alberta is a province to the east of British Columbia.

7. My family will take a trip to Banff next month.

8. Our neighbour will take care of our dog Mickey for us.

ISBN: 978-1-897164-31-0

D. Complete the card about yourself.

All the information you fill in should be proper nouns.

My name : _____

My birth month : _____

City I live in : _____

School I go to : _____

My favourite book : _____

My favourite movie : _____

My favourite festival : _____

Name of my father : _____

Name of my mother : _____

Name of my best friend : _____

Name of my pet (if any) : _____

A **Gaggle** of Geese?

Have you ever heard of a flock of sheep, a herd of buffalo, or a litter of kittens? You probably have. But have you ever heard of a pod of seals, a pride of lions, or a colony of penguins? What about a gaggle of geese?

We use different words to talk about different groups of animals. We can use words to talk about animals that are about the same size and type. For example, we can use the word "herd" to talk about buffalo, cattle, deer, and moose. We use the word "pack" to talk about wolves or wild dogs. We can use the word "flock" to talk about sheep and birds, but when we talk about a group of crows, we call them a murder of crows. Maybe that is because farmers don't like it when crows eat their crops.

What word do we use to talk about a group of fish? If we visit an aquarium, we might say: Look at the school of beautiful tropical fish! Yes...a school of fish! Do fish really go to school?

When we learn to use interesting words like this, people enjoy listening to us talk!

ISBN: 978-1-897164-31-0

A. Write the words in the correct places.

cattle   penguins
wolves   sheep   geese
fish   crows   lions   kittens   seals

1. a herd of _____
2. a school of _____
3. a colony of _____
4. a murder of _____
5. a pack of _____
6. a pride of _____
7. a flock of _____
8. a litter of _____
9. a gaggle of _____
10. a pod of _____

B. Draw a group of animals mentioned in the passage. Fill in the blanks to complete the title.

A _____ of _____

ISBN: 978-1-897164-31-0

Irregular Plural Nouns

For nouns ending in "y", change the "y" to "i" and add "es" to form the plural. For nouns ending in "f/fe", change the "f/fe" to "v" and add "es".

Examples: fairy → fairies   calf → calves   life → lives

Some plural nouns may spell the same as or completely different from their singular form.

Examples: salmon → salmon   ox → oxen

C.   **Circle the correct plural form for the first words.**

1. **foot**

foots
feet
feat

2. **deer**

deer
deeres
deers

3. **city**

citys
cityes
cities

4. **mouse**

mouses
mice
mousses

5. **knife**

knives
knifes
knifees

6. **family**

familys
famives
families

7. **tooth**

tooths
tooth
teeth

8. **leaf**

leaves
leaies
leafs

9. **offspring**

offspring
offsprings
offspringes

ISBN: 978-1-897164-31-0

D. **Complete the crossword puzzle with the plural form of the clue words.**

Across

A. bunny
B. shelf
C. loaf
D. medium
E. cod

Down

1. buffalo
2. cattle
3. sheep
4. moose
5. goose

The Goat
– Our Best Friend

People say that the dog is man's best friend. But goats are very important, too. In fact, people have kept goats for thousands of years – longer than we have kept dogs.

Goats are useful to us in many different ways. We can cut the hair from goats and spin it into wool. We can make clothing from the wool. One kind of wool made from goat hair is called cashmere. A cashmere sweater can be very expensive.

Goats also give milk, just like cows do! Did you know that more people around the world drink goat's milk than they do cow's milk? Goat's milk is easier for babies to drink. We make lovely cheese, such as feta, from goat's milk. Some people put goat's milk on their skin to keep it soft.

In many countries, goat's meat is eaten instead of beef or pork. We also use goatskin to make gloves and boots. Goatskin leather is very soft.

A female goat is called a doe or nanny. A male goat is called a buck or billy. Do you know what a baby goat is called? A kid!

With everything goats give to us, we can say that the goat is also our best friend. Don't you think so?

ISBN: 978-1-897164-31-0

A.   Write the names for the animals.

1.

2.

3.

B.   Read the passage.   Complete the diagram below with the given words.

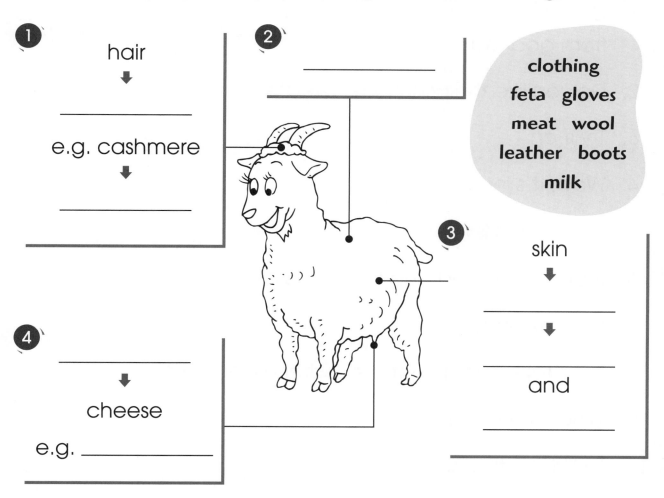

1   hair

⬇

_____

e.g. cashmere

⬇

_____

2   _____

clothing
feta   gloves
meat   wool
leather   boots
milk

3   skin

⬇

_____

⬇

and

_____

4   _____

⬇

cheese

e.g. _____

ISBN: 978-1-897164-31-0

Sentence Types

All sentences begin with capital letters.

A **telling sentence** tells about someone or something. It ends with a period. An **asking sentence** asks about someone or something. It ends with a question mark. A **surprising sentence** shows a strong feeling. It ends with an exclamation mark. An **imperative sentence** tells someone to do or not to do something. It ends with a period. The subject "you" is left out.

C. **Add the correct punctuation marks at the end of the sentences. Then write the letters.**

T – telling sentences
A – asking sentences
S – surprising sentences
I – imperative sentences

1. Cashmere is made from goat hair _____

2. Do you like this cashmere sweater _____

3. Try it on _____

4. Wow, it's incredibly soft _____

5. How much is it _____

6. It's one hundred and fifteen dollars _____

7. How expensive _____

8. Let's take a look at the sweaters over there _____

9. What are they made of _____

10. I will take the blue one _____

ISBN: 978-1-897164-31-0

D.   Write what they are saying.

1. Surprising Sentence

    _____

2. Telling Sentence

    _____

3. Asking Sentence

    _____

4. Imperative Sentence

    _____

5. Imperative Sentence

    _____

6. Surprising Sentence

    _____

ISBN: 978-1-897164-31-0

The Narwhal
A Real-Life Unicorn

We love unicorns, but they are not real animals. We can find unicorns only in fairy tales.

Don't be sad. There is a real-life unicorn here on Earth. It is the narwhal. A narwhal is not a horse with a long horn, but a whale!

The narwhal can be found in the waters around Canada and other northern countries. There are not very many of them, so if you see one, you are lucky! They can grow to be five metres long. They are blue-grey with white blotches. They are brown when they are born. Narwhals like to swim with their friends, and talk to one another using sound waves, like other whales.

All narwhals have two teeth in their upper jaw. But the male narwhal's left tooth starts to grow outwards after it is one year old. This tooth twists as it grows. It just grows and grows, and can be up to three metres long! We can call it a tusk. We are not sure what it is used for.

Narwhals are amazing animals – and they are real!

ISBN: 978-1-897164-31-0

A. Find words from the passage for the meanings below.

1. having good fortune

2. without doubts

3. very long, pointed tooth

4. very surprising

5. not imagined

6. the biggest sea mammals

7. turns

8. large discoloured marks

B. Complete the chart.

The Narwhal

Length: up to 1._____ long

Colour: (grown-up) 2._____ with 3._____

(baby) 4._____

Live in: waters around 5._____ and 6._____

Way of communication: 7._____

ISBN: 978-1-897164-31-0

Subjects and Predicates

A sentence has two main parts – a subject and a predicate.

The **subject** tells whom or what the sentence is about. The **predicate** tells what the subject is or what the subject does.

Example: Many children | love fairy tales.
        (subject)   (predicate)

C. **Draw a vertical line between the subject and the predicate in each sentence.**

1. My class is doing a project on the narwhal.

2. Mrs. Reid told us to look for information about the narwhal on the Internet.

3. The narwhal is a whale.

4. The left tooth of the male narwhal can grow up to three metres long.

5. The female is slightly smaller than the male.

6. The skin of a baby narwhal is brown in colour.

7. You may see a narwhal in the Arctic seas.

8. Fish, squid, and shrimps are what narwhals eat.

9. I think a narwhal really looks like a unicorn.

  ISBN: 978-1-897164-31-0

D.   Fill in the blanks with the correct subjects.

the fairy tale   Bruce   we
the main character
our teacher   the unicorn

1. _____ told us a fairy tale.

2. _____ in the story is called Bruce.

3. _____ met a brave unicorn in a forest.

4. _____ is called Anston.

5. _____ has a happy ending.

6. _____ all enjoyed listening to this story.

E.   Write predicates to complete the sentences.

1. My sister _____ .

2. The movie _____ .

3. The theme song _____ .

4. Tim and Matt _____ .

5. The whales _____ .

6. Everyone _____ .

ISBN: 978-1-897164-31-0

Skipping Rope

Skipping rope is fun to play for boys and girls. It is also a good form of exercise. You can skip by yourself or skip with friends. You can skip fast or slowly. You can skip in an easy way or a difficult way. Skipping is a great sport!

When you are skipping with friends, try skipping while you all say this chant. The skipper can also do some actions to match the words:

Teddy Bear, Teddy Bear, turn around.
Teddy Bear, Teddy Bear, touch the ground.
Teddy Bear, Teddy Bear, touch your head.
Teddy Bear, Teddy Bear, go to bed!

Here's another chant. Jump in and then say:

Apples! Peaches! Bananas! Plums!
Tell me when your birthday comes!

You then skip "pepper" (really fast skipping) and shout out the months of the year: January, February, March... You jump out when you come to the month of your birthday. Try not to get caught in the skipping rope before then!

ISBN: 978-1-897164-31-0

A. Circle the words in the word search.

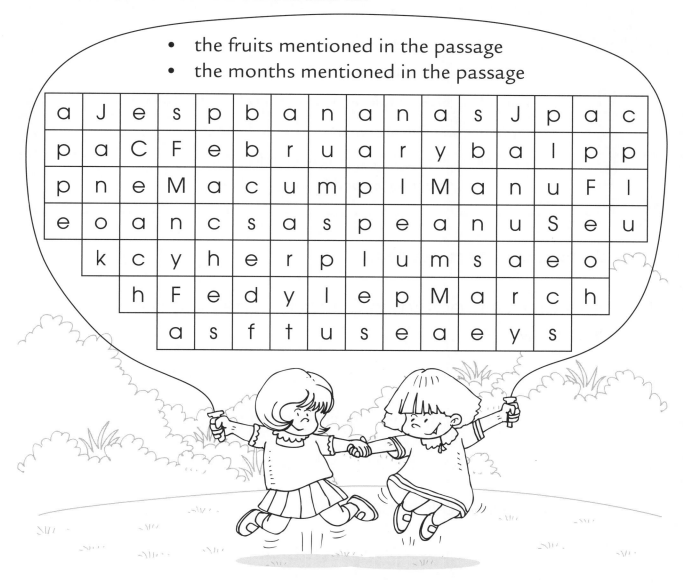

- the fruits mentioned in the passage
- the months mentioned in the passage

a	J	e	s	p	b	a	n	a	n	a	s	J	p	a	c
p	a	C	F	e	b	r	u	a	r	y	b	a	l	p	p
p	n	e	M	a	c	u	m	p	l	M	a	n	u	F	l
e	o	a	n	c	s	a	s	p	e	a	n	u	S	e	u
	k	c	y	h	e	r	p	l	u	m	s	a	e	o	
	h	F	e	d	y	l	e	p	M	a	r	c	h		
	a	s	f	t	u	s	e	a	e	y	s				

B. Fill in the blanks with words from the passage.

1. Skipping is a kind of _____ .

2. You can skip with your _____ .

3. You can skip while saying a _____ .

4. The _____ can do some actions while skipping.

5. Be careful not to get _____ in the skipping rope.

ISBN: 978-1-897164-31-0

Commas

Commas can be used to:

· separate items in a list.

　　Example:　Blue, purple, and pink are my favourite colours.

· introduce and follow quotations.

　　Examples:　Ben said, "Skipping is good for you."

　　　　　　　"Skipping is good for you," said Ben.

C.　Add commas where needed.

1.　There are four seasons in Canada.　They are spring summer fall and winter.

2.　June July and August are the summer months in Ontario.

3.　I like skipping swimming cycling and rock climbing.

4.　Sarah asked "Would you like to skip with me?"

5.　"Let's ask Jerry to join us" I said.

6.　She reminded me "Don't forget to take your skipping rope with you."

7.　We sell all kinds of fruits: apples oranges bananas peaches cherries mangoes – you name it.

 ISBN: 978-1-897164-31-0

Quotation Marks

Quotation marks are used in pairs. They can be used to:

· contain the exact words of a speaker.

Example: "Your skipping rope looks nice," I told Liz.

· draw attention to a term that is used in a special way in the context.

Example: We skipped "pepper" and shouted out the months.

D. Check ✔ if the quotation marks are used correctly in the sentences.

1. Is Oshawa one of the "bedroom communities" of Ontario?

2. "How many times can you skip in a minute? he asked me."

3. Our coach always reminds us, "Practice makes perfect."

4. "Halifax" is the capital city of Nova Scotia.

5. This lake "swallows" all the water from the river.

6. The berries are the "jewels" of this dessert.

7. Dad said, "When the sun sets," we'll have to leave.

ISBN: 978-1-897164-31-0

I Love Haiku!

I am a poet. I write all kinds of poems: acrostic poems, rhyming poems, non-rhyming poems... But my favourite kind of poem is called haiku.

Haiku is a Japanese word. It means "short verse". Haiku poems are very short! People have been writing them for centuries. They are made with only three lines. The first and last lines should have five syllables. The middle line should have seven syllables.

A man named Basho, from Japan, wrote the first haiku poem. His most famous poem is about a frog. This is how you say his poem in Japanese:

Furu ike ya
Kawazu tobikomu
mizu no oto

In English, we can say:

There is an old pond
A frog goes jumping in it
The sound of water

Writing a short haiku is not easy. It takes practice to write a poem about something in only three lines!

ISBN: 978-1-897164-31-0

A. Check ✔ the poem that is a haiku.

1. *Chicken wings*
    Chicken wings
    We all love them fried
    Yummy!

2. *One two three*
    Apple trees
    Growing tall in the green green meadow

3. *Summertime is great*
    Let's go swimming at the beach
    Do you love it not?

B. Change the underlined words in the sentences to make them correct.

1. The writer loves writing <u>stories</u>.   _____

2. Haiku is a kind of <u>long</u> verse.   _____

3. There are <u>four</u> lines in a haiku.   _____

4. Basho was a man from <u>England</u>.   _____

5. Basho's most famous haiku is
    about a <u>toad</u>.   _____

ISBN: 978-1-897164-31-0

Syllables

A **syllable** is an individual sound segment in a word. Words can have one or more syllables.

Examples: frog (1 syllable)   water (2 syllables)

favourite (3 syllables)   kindergarten (4 syllables)

C.   Say the things.   Write the number of syllables in the boxes.

1.

2.

3.

4.

5.

6.

7.

8.

9.

ISBN: 978-1-897164-31-0

D. Say the words. Write them on the correct lines.

> acrostic famous Japanese sound
> competition lollipop information
> book bright stationery pizza author

1 Syllable _____

2 Syllables _____

3 Syllables _____

4 Syllables _____

E. Use "/" to separate the syllables in these words.

> *If the word has a double consonant, each letter in the double consonant belongs to different syllables. Example: puz/zle*

1. s y l l a b l e

2. g a r a g e

3. a f t e r n o o n

4. c o l o u r f u l

5. c a r r y   6. e x c i t i n g

7. i n v i s i b l e   8. n e c e s s a r y

ISBN: 978-1-897164-31-0

Sometimes our body does things we don't ask it to do. Sneezing, coughing, blinking, and even yawning are examples of *involuntary movements* or *reflex actions*. What makes our body do these things?

These involuntary actions are a response to a *stimulus*. Believe it or not, when we do these things, our body is trying to protect itself. If an irritant such as pollen from plants gets into our nose or nasal passages, our body sneezes to get it out. If we breathe in dust, our body coughs to remove it from our lungs or windpipe. We blink in order to keep our eyes clean and moist and to prevent dust and other objects from settling on them. A yawn is our body's way of making us put more oxygen into our bloodstream.

What tells our body to take care of us the way it does? These involuntary movements occur because our brain is giving out signals. There is a system of nerves, the *central nervous system*, that covers our entire body: from the brain, down the spinal cord inside our spinal column (the column of bones that goes down our back), to the very tips of our fingers and toes. When our body parts sense certain things, like a mosquito bite, a message is sent to our brain. Then the brain sends a message back to itch.

Without these reflex actions, we would not be able to live very long.

Why Do We Sneeze?

ISBN: 978-1-897164-31-0

A. Read the sentences. Complete the crossword puzzle with words from the passage.

- 3 actions or C movements are things that our body does without our asking it to do.

- Our body responds to a 4 on its own in order to A itself.

- Our body sneezes or 5 to get rid of an 1 .

- D is a way to keep our eyes clean and moist.

- We 2 to put more oxygen into our bloodstream.

- Our body parts send messages to our B through the central E system.

ISBN: 978-1-897164-31-0

Subject Pronouns

A **subject pronoun** acts as the subject in a sentence.

"I", "you", "we", "they", "he", "she", and "it" are subject pronouns.

Example: Our body is amazing. <u>It</u> does things to protect us.

B. **Fill in the blanks with the correct subject pronouns for the underlined words to complete the sentences.**

1. <u>Our eyes</u> are very important to us. _____ enable us to see.

2. <u>Mom and I</u> have an appointment with Dr. Amo. _____ will have our eyes checked.

3. <u>Our central nervous system</u> is very complicated. _____ covers our whole body.

4. <u>Tommy</u> has got some mosquito bites on his legs. _____ feels very itchy now.

5. Kingsley has left <u>you</u> the message. _____ don't have to call him back.

6. <u>Betsy</u> did not sleep well last night. _____ keeps yawning the whole morning.

7. Mom has bought <u>me</u> some cough syrup. _____ will have to take some before bed.

 ISBN: 978-1-897164-31-0

Object Pronouns

An **object pronoun** acts as an object that receives the action of the verb or to whom or what the verb is directed in a sentence.

"Me", "you", "us", "them", "him", "her", and "it" are object pronouns.

Example: Miss Carter told <u>us</u> about our body's reflex actions.

C.   Check ✔ if the underlined object pronouns are correct. Otherwise, correct the wrong ones and write them on the lines.

1.   Lester has given <u>her</u> a diary. I write in it every night.

_____

2.   Mrs. Carlos has made some cream puffs for us. I have put <u>it</u> in the fridge.   _____

3.   I gave <u>him</u> the key yesterday. Where have you put it?   _____

4.   The riddle was not difficult. Hilda could solve <u>it</u> very quickly.   _____

5.   Martha is having a swimming class now. We'll meet <u>her</u> in the afternoon.   _____

6.   Is the actor here yet? I really want to see <u>us</u>.   _____

7.   Dad has promised to take <u>him</u> to the zoo when we finish the project.   _____

Girl's Festival *in Japan*

3rd March

Dear Sammy,

Today is a special day. We call it *Hina Matsuri*. "Hina" means "dolls" and "matsuri" means "festival". We also call this day "Girl's Festival". It is a special day for us girls. On this day, our families will wish us success and happiness. We will put special dolls on display in our homes. My doll set has 15 dolls and it used to be my grandmother's! It is very beautiful.

We also have peach blossoms in our house for Girl's Festival. Yesterday, my mother took me to the flower market to buy some. Peach blossoms are a lovely pink colour. I love pink, do you?

I like to wear my kimono on Hina Matsuri. I am going to have a little tea party at my house today, too. My grandmother will make some sushi for us to eat. Do you like sushi?

Happy Girl's Festival, Sammy! I wish you success and happiness!

Sayonara (this means goodbye)!

Your friend,

Kiyoka

ISBN: 978-1-897164-31-0

A. **Circle the things related to Girl's Festival.**

B. **Draw lines to match the two parts.**

1. hina	•	• Girl's Festival
2. matsuri	•	• goodbye
3. Hina Matsuri	•	• a kind of pink flowers
4. peach blossoms	•	• festival
5. kimono	•	• dolls
6. sayonara	•	• a kind of Japanese clothing for girls and women

ISBN: 978-1-897164-31-0

Possessive Nouns

A **possessive noun** shows possession.

For a singular noun or a plural noun not ending in "s", add an apostrophe and an "s" at the end of the noun.

Example: Miss Reid's folder is yellow. The children's folders are blue.

For a plural noun ending in "s", add only an apostrophe.

Example: The students' performance was outstanding.

C.   Circle the correct possessive nouns to complete the sentences.

1.   Girls's / Girl's   Festival is on 3rd March every year.

2.   Kiyoka's / Kiyoka'   doll set is awesome.

3.   It was her   grandma's / grandmas'   doll set.

4.   The   dolls's / dolls'   clothes are beautiful.

5.   Her   sister's / sisters's   kimono is too big for her.

6.   Her   friends' / friends's   parents will also join the tea party.

7.   Mr. and Mrs.   Tanaka's / Tanaka'   home is also decorated with peach blossoms.

8.   Their   daughters's / daughter's   favourite doll is the empress.

 ISBN: 978-1-897164-31-0

Possessive Adjectives

A **possessive adjective** describes a noun that follows it. It tells who possesses or is related to the noun.

"My", "your", "our", "their", "his", "her", and "its" are possessive adjectives.

Example: You have to put <u>your</u> books away.

D. Fill in the blanks with the correct possessive adjectives.

1. Yumi and I are saving money to buy a doll set. We will put _____ doll set in the living room.

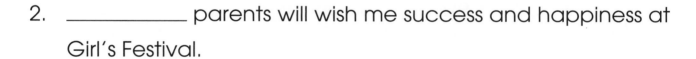

2. _____ parents will wish me success and happiness at Girl's Festival.

3. Mom likes making sushi. _____ sushi is delicious.

4. Dad will drive _____ car to the flower market to get some peach blossoms.

5. Our dog likes the scent of peach blossoms. It always wags _____ tail when it gets close to the plant.

6. My friends will all wear _____ kimonos to the tea party.

7. Will you tell _____ friends about Girl's Festival?

ISBN: 978-1-897164-31-0

A Visit to the
Seniors' Centre

My mom works on Saturdays, so every Saturday morning my babysitter, Jenny, takes me somewhere interesting. Once she took me to the aquarium, and then she made me do a project about my favourite fish.

Today Jenny took me to a seniors' centre. There were a lot of old people there. Some of them were in wheelchairs. Some of them couldn't see or hear very well. Jenny introduced me to some of the people. Then she asked me if I would read the newspaper to them. I spoke loudly so they could hear me well. They said my reading was excellent. I felt proud.

Later, Jenny and I had lunch with them. I sat at a table with four people. During lunch, they told me about their lives. One man had been a soldier in World War II! He fought in France. The two ladies at my table had grown up in other countries. Mrs. Ip grew up in China, and Mrs. Guleed is from Somalia. They told me a little bit about life in their old countries. I thought it seemed hard.

After lunch, Jenny played the piano. Some of the people sang along to the music. The people at the seniors' centre were very interesting and very kind to me. I told Jenny that I would like to go back to the seniors' centre next Saturday.

ISBN: 978-1-897164-31-0

A. Put the events in order. Write the letters in the boxes.

A The writer had lunch with the people.

B The writer read the newspaper to some people.

C A man and two women told the writer about their lives.

D Jenny introduced the writer to some people at a seniors' centre.

E Jenny played the piano and some people sang along.

☐ ➡ ☐ ➡ ☐ ➡ ☐ ➡ ☐

B. Answer the following questions.

1. What did Jenny ask the writer to do after their trip to the aquarium?

_____

_____

2. Why did the writer read the newspaper loudly?

_____

3. Why did the writer want to go back to the seniors' centre again?

_____

_____

Demonstrative Pronouns

A **demonstrative pronoun** shows or points to someone or something.

Use "this" or "these" for someone or something near you.
Use "that" or "those" for someone or something farther away.

Example: These flowers are lilacs and those over there are daffodils.

C.   Fill in the blanks with the correct demonstrative pronouns.

1.   Jenny looked at the sketchbook in front of her and said, "Is _____ the project I asked you to do?"

2.   Jenny pointed to the building at the far end of the road and said, "_____ is where we are going today."

3.   Let's go and talk with _____ people over there.

4.   "_____ is today's newspaper," Jenny said as she handed the newspaper to Victor.

5.   Could you pass me _____ folk?

6.   "_____ vegetables are delicious," Victor said as he started eating.

ISBN: 978-1-897164-31-0

Possessive Pronouns

A **possessive pronoun** tells who possesses something or is related to someone.

"Mine", "yours", "ours", "theirs", "his", and "hers" are possessive pronouns.

Example: Those are our bikes.

Those bikes are <u>ours</u>.

D.   Rewrite the sentences using possessive pronouns.

1. This is my book.

    _____

2. These are Jerry's stickers.

    _____

3. Is this your lunch box?

    _____

4. Those are Lisa's shoes.

    _____

5. That is our puppy.

    _____

6. These are Mr. and Mrs. Newman's pictures.

    _____

A. Derek meets Willy the Wizard in his dream. Willy promises to grant Derek a wish if he can go through some challenges. Help Derek complete the first challenge.

Say these things. Write their names. Circle the silent consonants and underline the long vowel digraphs in the words. I've put some pictures here to trick you. So be careful!

1. _____

2. _____

3. _____

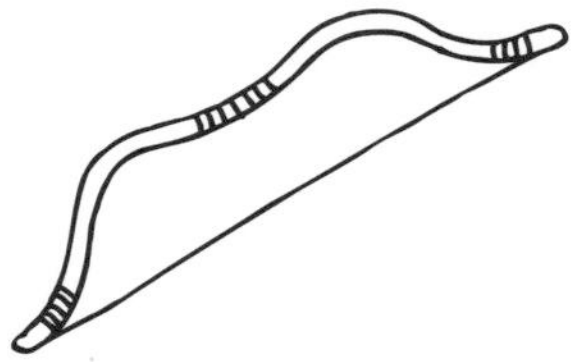

4. _____

5. _____

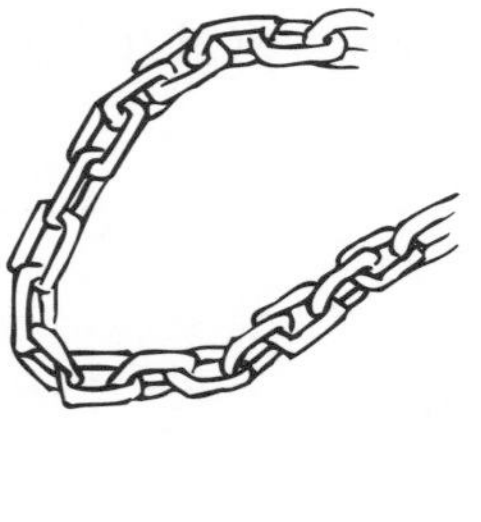

6. _____

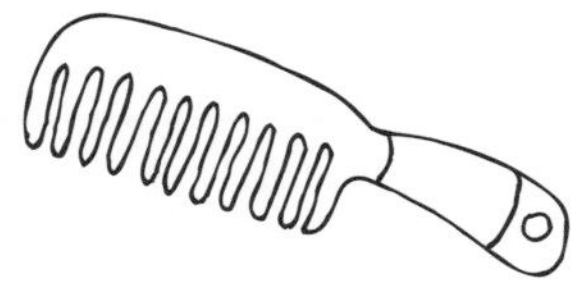

7. _____

8. _____

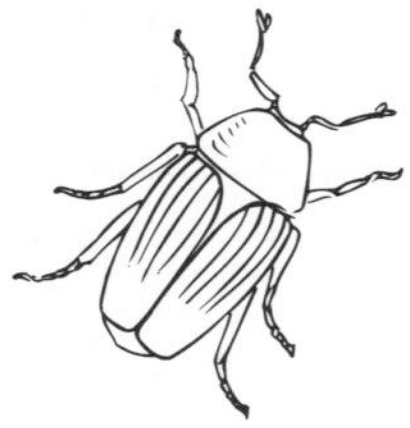

ISBN: 978-1-897164-31-0

B. **Here's the second challenge. Help Derek put the words in the correct places.**

baby   rhyme

carpet   hyphen

cookie   gypsy

goose   cycle

candle   citizen

puppy   garage

gem   golf

cent

Some of the words can be put in more than one box.

With a Hard "C" Sound	
With a Soft "C" Sound	
With a Hard "G" Sound	
With a Soft "G" Sound	
"Y" with a Long "E" Sound	
"Y" with a Long "I" Sound	

ISBN: 978-1-897164-31-0

C. In this challenge, Derek has to go through a maze. Help Derek write the number of syllables in the circles of only the correctly spelled plural nouns to get to the exit. Draw his route.

luggages

foots

information

advices

media

salmon

carries

halves

receives

babys

rhino

blueberries

elfs

furnitures

evidence

Be careful! Some of the words are not nouns.

Exit

 ISBN: 978-1-897164-31-0

D. **Help Derek go through this challenge by replacing the underlined subject in each sentence with a rhyming word.**

1. The <u>rate</u> is very high.

    _____

2. Her <u>jeans</u> are green.

    _____

3. This <u>tie</u> is for Daddy.

    _____

4. The red <u>meat</u> is very fresh.

    _____

5. The <u>mug</u> is filled with water.

    _____

6. This <u>hen</u> belongs to Mrs. Howell.

    _____

7. The <u>hall</u> is right behind the church.

    _____

8. <u>Bricks</u> were used to build this model.

    _____

9. The <u>frog</u> is getting bigger and bigger.

    _____

The sentence should make sense after the change.

ISBN: 978-1-897164-31-0

E. **Help Derek add back the missing punctuation marks to complete this challenge.**

I have taken out all the commas and quotation marks in these sentences. Add them back in the correct places.

1. Don't forget to turn off the light Mom reminded me.

2. This is the core part of the computer said Brian.

3. Miss Hall said You'll need a balloon a marker and some buttons.

4. We'll go to Lake Simcoe Niagara Falls or Wasaga Beach this weekend Dad told us.

5. Moose hippos cheetahs and black bears are some of the animals you can see at the zoo.

6. I'd like to join you said Anne Jimmy and Lester together.

7. The government encourages all office buildings to go green to protect the environment.

 ISBN: 978-1-897164-31-0

F. Help Derek go through the last challenge by filling in the blanks and writing the missing sentences.

1. That is Karen's teddy bear.

That is _____ teddy bear.

That teddy bear is hers.

2. This is _____ picture.

This is their picture.

Mr. and Mrs. Alden

_____

3. These are Dave's marbles.

_____

_____

You've gone through all the challenges. Write a telling sentence about your wish and it'll be granted.

My Wish

_____

_____

_____

ISBN: 978-1-897164-31-0

Dear Ms. Naughton,

My name is Emi. I am a grade three student at Primrose School. You used to be the principal of this school. My teacher, Mrs. Rao, told us to write a letter to you today. She said you are retired now, so you need things to do. Is it true? Are you bored? What do you do now? My grandpa likes to play golf. Maybe you should try it.

Love,
Emi King

A Letter to – and from –
Ms. Naughton

Dear Emi,

Thank you so much for your lovely letter. I have been getting so much mail this week. Mrs. Rao is correct. I am retired now. I miss my students and teachers very much.

I am not bored, Emi, but my life is very different. I do volunteer work at the hospital twice a week. I also go for a long walk every day with my friends. I am doing some interesting work at the library, too. And I am thinking about writing a book about being a principal for 30 years – I have a lot of funny stories to tell! When the weather gets warmer, I will try to do some golfing. My son is a good golfer and he can teach me.

Thank you again for your thoughtful letter, my dear.

Love,
Margaret Naughton

ISBN: 978-1-897164-31-0

A. Complete the following about Ms. Naughton.

What Ms. Naughton is doing:

1. _____

2. _____

3. _____

What Ms. Naughton is planning to do:

4. _____

5. _____

B. Imagine you were another student at Primrose School. Write a letter to Ms. Naughton and suggest what other things she can do.

Dear Ms. Naughton,

_____

_____

_____

_____

_____

_____

_____

_____

Subject-Verb Agreement

The **verb** must **agree** with its **subject** in a sentence.

If the subject is singular, a singular verb should be used.

Example: Ms. Naughton <u>is</u> retired now.

If the subject is plural, a plural verb should be used.

Example: <u>The children</u> <u>write</u> letters to her every month.

C.   Circle the correct verbs to complete the sentences.

1. Ms. Naughton help / helps at the library every Saturday.

2. She invite / invites an author to read stories to children every week.

3. Some authors wear / wears funny costumes.

4. Others use / uses interesting props as they read / reads .

5. Ms. Naughton then ask / asks the children to draw a book cover for the story.

6. Each week, she and the author choose / chooses the best design and put / puts it on a beautifully decorated board.

7. There is / are now 11 pictures on the board.

ISBN: 978-1-897164-31-0

D. **Check ✔ if the underlined verbs are correct. Otherwise, correct the wrong ones and write them on the lines.**

1. Emi and her family <u>live</u> just a block away from Primrose School.

    _____

2. Emi's little sister Liz also <u>go</u> to that school.

    _____

3. The playground at the school <u>are</u> big.

    _____

4. Liz <u>likes</u> to play with Emi and her friends at recess.

    _____

5. Emi's friends also <u>enjoys</u> playing with her.

    _____

E. **Change the subject of each sentence to plural. Rewrite the sentence with the correct verb form. Make other changes where needed.**

1. The kitten drinks the milk happily.

    _____

    _____

2. The child is looking at the ladybug.

    _____

3. The pastry tastes sweet and delicious.

    _____

4. The girl puts away her book.

    _____

ISBN: 978-1-897164-31-0

The Sugar Shack

I had a great day yesterday. My parents took my brother and me to the Sugar Shack. We go there every spring.

My dad said that the weather would be perfect for a good sugaring-off. For a week there were sunny days and cold, frosty nights. Dad said this kind of weather would get the sap running in the maple trees. He was right!

There were red, silver, and sugar maple trees as far as I could see, and most of them had little wooden buckets hanging on them. We collected the watery sap that dripped out of the maple trees through spigots bored into the tree trunks. This is the old-fashioned way. People in many other places use tubes and vacuum pumps to collect the sap now.

Then we went to a large campfire in the snow. The woman poured the sap we collected into a big iron pot. A man was stirring and stirring. We watched the sap cook. Slowly it got thicker and darker. It was turning into delicious sweet-smelling maple syrup!

When it was done, we sat at a picnic table outdoors and ate plates of pancakes, sausages, ham, baked beans, and scrambled eggs with our maple syrup. My parents put maple syrup in their coffee, too! We ate for as long as we could. Then we went for a long walk in the maple woods.

ISBN: 978-1-897164-31-0

A. Circle the things the family ate on the picnic at the Sugar Shack.

baked beans   bacon   sausages

ham   corned beef   fried eggs

waffles   pancakes   scrambled eggs

B. Find words from the passage that mean the same as the words below.

1. small

2. correct

3. excellent

4. ready

5. gathered

6. method

7. pails

8. outside

9. tasty

ISBN: 978-1-897164-31-0

Past Tense Verbs

Most **past tense verbs** are formed by adding "d" or "ed" to the base form. Some are formed by repeating the last letter before adding "ed". Others remain the same or have completely different spellings.

Examples: dance → danced   pour → poured
                drip → dripped   put → put
                go → went

C. Complete the crossword puzzle with the past form of the clue words.

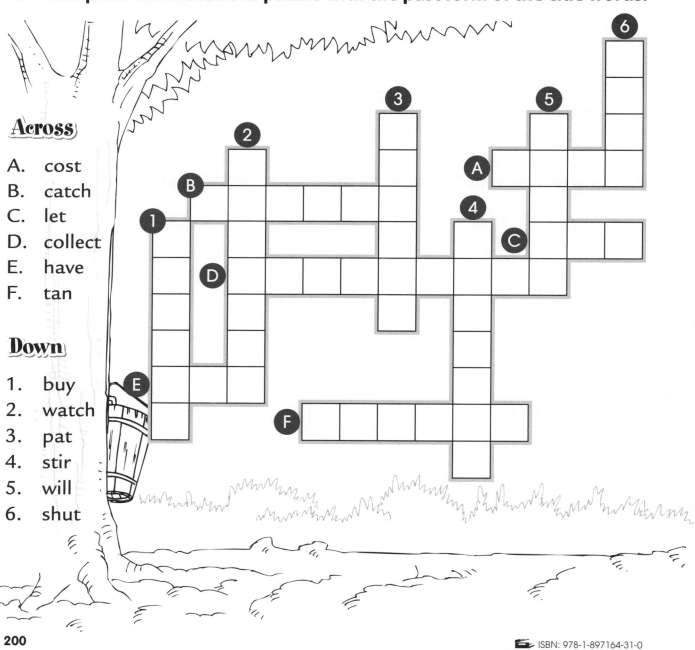

Across

A. cost
B. catch
C. let
D. collect
E. have
F. tan

Down

1. buy
2. watch
3. pat
4. stir
5. will
6. shut

ISBN: 978-1-897164-31-0

D. Fill in the blanks with the past form of the given verbs.

For some verbs ending in "y", change the "y" to "i" before adding "ed".

Yesterday morning, Mom (promise) 1._____ to make pancakes for us as afternoon snacks, so after school, my brother and I (hurry) 2._____ home.

When we (arrive) 3._____ home, we (be) 4._____ delighted to see the pancakes on the kitchen table. I (grab) 5._____ the maple syrup we (buy) 6._____ from the Sugar Shack and (pour) 7._____ some on my pancakes. My brother (do) 8._____ the same on his after me. The golden brown fluid (spread) 9._____ all over our pancakes. We (devour) 10._____ our treats at once. I (eat) 11._____ so fast that I nearly (choke) 12._____ . My brother (look) 13._____ scared at first. When he (know) 14._____ that I (be) 15._____ all right, we (burst) 16._____ into laughter together.

The Amazing Coconut

Do you know what an amazing fruit the coconut is? Maybe you have seen small, round, and brown coconuts in the fruit section of the supermarket. Maybe you have made coconut macaroons, and needed to buy a bag of dried, shredded, white coconut meat. We call this coconut meat *copra*. It is a tasty and healthy snack.

Coconuts grow on palm trees. But the small, round coconuts you see in the supermarket grows inside a larger pod, or husk. This large husk is a tough fibre called coir. We use coir to make ropes, yarn, and carpets. Coir is even used to make aquarium filters, flower pots, soundproofing, and mattresses!

Coconut oil comes from copra. This oil is used in making some snack foods and is quite a healthy oil to eat. Coconut oil is also used in suntan lotions and other cosmetics that we put on our skin.

Many people love coconut milk. You can buy it in cans or make it yourself by adding a cup of boiling water to a bag of dried coconut and putting it into the blender, but you must strain out the bits after.

There is coconut water inside the coconut. It has more vitamins and fewer calories than milk or orange juice. And best of all...coconut water is delicious.

ISBN: 978-1-897164-31-0

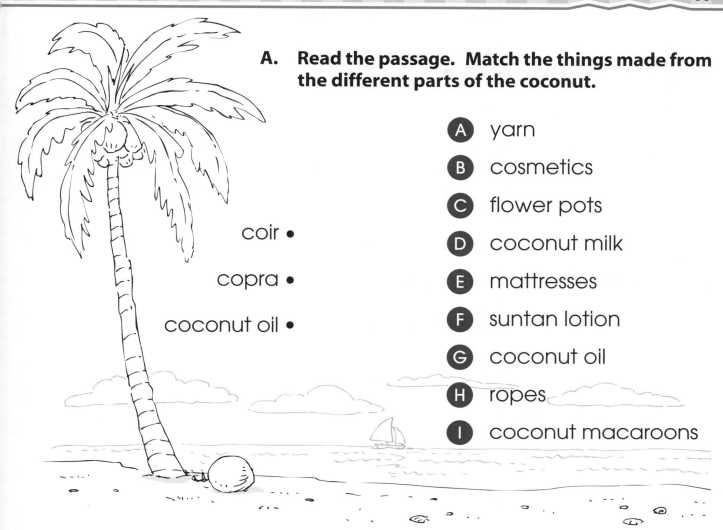

A. Read the passage. Match the things made from the different parts of the coconut.

coir •

copra •

coconut oil •

A yarn

B cosmetics

C flower pots

D coconut milk

E mattresses

F suntan lotion

G coconut oil

H ropes

I coconut macaroons

B. Complete the recipe.

Coconut Milk

DRIED COCONUT

Ingredients: 1 bag of dried coconut
1 cup of boiling water

Steps:

1. _____

2. _____

3. _____

ISBN: 978-1-897164-31-0

Adjectives

An **adjective** describes a noun.

We use adjectives to add interest and detail to our writing.

Example: Mom bought a coconut from the superstore.

Mom bought a <u>small</u>, <u>round</u> coconut from the <u>new</u> superstore.

C.   Circle the adjectives in the sentences.

1.   The coconut is an amazing fruit.

2.   It has white meat inside a large, hard husk.

3.   A young coconut is green with tender meat.

4.   The water inside the coconut is healthy and refreshing.

5.   The coconut is very useful and can be used to make many things.

6.   Coir can be used to make strong ropes.

7.   The brown pots are also made from this tough fibre.

8.   The dried, shredded meat can be used to make delicious macaroons.

ISBN: 978-1-897164-31-0

D.   Fill in the blanks with the correct adjectives.

bright   wet   early   slimy   stuffy

crowded   colourful   tall   big   cold

1. A _____ coconut fell from the _____ tree.

2. The _____ snail is moving slowly on the _____ mud.

3. The heat from the _____ sun warms the _____ water.

4. _____ tulips start blooming in _____ spring.

5. The air is _____ in the _____ room.

E.   Add adjectives to the sentences to make them more interesting.

1. The children played happily in the water.

   _____

   _____

2. We went to the restaurant for dinner.

   _____

   _____

3. The birds are chirping in the tree.

   _____

   _____

ISBN: 978-1-897164-31-0

Shooting Stars

Shooting stars are not stars – and they don't shoot! They are rocks, called meteors, that come towards the Earth from far away in space. These meteors can be any size, large or small.

A meteor flies through space at a very high speed, up to 200 000 kilometres per hour! When things go this fast through the air around the Earth, everything becomes very hot. The air around the rock gets so hot it glows blue-white. This blue-white streak in the sky is what we see, and it is why we call it a "shooting star".

As a meteor shoots through the sky, it breaks into pieces. Usually this "shooting star" will disappear in less than a second. But some meteors are larger and do not break up completely. Some bits of rock will crash into the Earth. When this happens, we call them meteorites. Most meteorites fall into the ocean.

Seeing a shooting star is an amazing thing. We think it is lucky to see one. The truth is, shooting stars happen often, but they move so fast that we often miss them if we are not looking carefully.

Have you ever seen a shooting star? If not, why not take the time to sit back and watch the sky the next time the stars are shining bright and clear? If you watch carefully and concentrate, you will surely see a shooting star. Don't forget to make a wish!

ISBN: 978-1-897164-31-0

A. Read the sentences. Circle the answers in the word search.

- Shooting stars are ___ that fly through ___ at very high speed.

- These rocks are called ___ .

- The ___ air around a fast flying meteor forms a blue-white ___ .

- ___ are bits of meteors that crash into the ___ .

- Seeing a shooting star is something ___ . You can make a ___ when you see one.

- You need to ___ if you want to see a shooting star.

q	m	E	a	r	h	e	c	i	d	h	m	e	t	o	l
m	e	t	e	o	r	s	o	q	c	r	e	c	k	j	b
o	r	d	s	c	k	p	n	s	h	a	t	n	a	s	p
h	o	e	t	k	E	a	r	t	h	E	e	h	o	c	f
j	k	a	r	s	p	c	s	r	n	a	o	s	m	e	d
l	e	m	e	c	o	n	c	e	n	t	r	a	t	e	g
s	p	a	o	e	c	t	i	a	z	g	i	c	o	t	k
h	t	z	b	a	e	s	v	k	l	r	t	e	i	r	p
b	c	i	s	g	t	p	g	h	a	m	e	t	t	e	o
r	o	n	s	t	r	a	q	j	w	i	s	h	o	c	m
e	n	g	i	p	m	c	o	n	c	t	r	o	c	s	f
n	t	k	d	i	E	e	a	t	h	p	h	t	i	k	j
i	s	t	a	e	k	n	b	a	m	a	s	e	l	g	c

Adverbs

An **adverb** describes a verb. It tells how an action takes place.

Most adverbs are formed by adding "ly" to the adjective. Others are irregular.

Example: The rock did not break up <u>completely</u> and fell <u>fast</u> into the ocean.

B. **Check ✔ if the underlined words in the sentences are adverbs.**

1. If you look <u>carefully</u>, you can see quite a number of shooting stars in a clear night.

2. People <u>often</u> scream when they see a shooting star.

3. That star looks so <u>lonely</u> in the night sky.

4. We'll <u>surely</u> see the full moon tonight.

5. I tried <u>hard</u> to concentrate but I still couldn't see a shooting star.

6. That's a <u>lovely</u> story about the stars.

7. We <u>usually</u> stay up to watch the stars when we go camping.

8. The weather <u>soon</u> cleared up and the stars started twinkling again.

ISBN: 978-1-897164-31-0

C. **Change the adjectives in parentheses ( ) to adverbs to complete the sentences.**

1. Jane asked her dad (eager) _____ when he would get her a telescope.

2. Mary and Sandra are working (patient) _____ on a jigsaw puzzle of different groups of stars.

3. The plane soared (high) _____ and disappeared behind the clouds.

4. Terry arrived (late) _____ and missed the meteor shower.

5. The leaves danced (graceful) _____ in the light breeze.

D. **Write sentences of your own with the given adverbs.**

1. stealthily
    _____
    _____

2. gladly
    _____
    _____

3. hard
    _____
    _____

ISBN: 978-1-897164-31-0

Aunt Jamilla is a student at the National Circus School in Montreal. She has very busy days. She has to take classes about anatomy and about nutrition. She is also taking French lessons, and music and rhythm lessons. She does a lot of stretching all day long. She says stretching is very important, especially for circus performers. She takes classes about learning to balance. She can balance on balls, on chairs, on a tight wire, and on a slack wire, too.

In her "acrobatics" class, Aunt Jamilla uses a trampoline, ladders, chairs, and something called a teeterboard. In her class called "aerials", she learns to work on a trapeze. She is also learning how to climb ribbons and swing around on them, like doing a dance in the air.

In her clowning arts class, Aunt Jamilla learns how to fall without getting hurt. She also learns how to "talk" with her body. She is also learning to juggle – not only with her hands, but with her feet!

Soon Aunt Jamilla will finish her classes. Then she will have her diploma of National Circus School Studies. With her experience, she will be able to find a job. It is Aunt Jamilla's dream to perform with the famous Cirque du Soleil someday. It is my dream to watch her do it.

The Circus School

ISBN: 978-1-897164-31-0

A. Write what classes Aunt Jamilla takes at the National Circus School.

Circus School

1. ___anatomy class___
2. _____
3. _____
4. _____
5. _____
6. _____
7. _____
8. _____

B. What do you want to learn most at a circus school? Why?

_____
_____
_____
_____
_____

ISBN: 978-1-897164-31-0

Prepositions

Some **prepositions** tell where something happens. Others tell when something happens.

Examples: Aunt Jamilla takes classes <u>at</u> the National Circus School. (where)

She started her studies there <u>in</u> 2005. (when)

C. Circle the prepositions. Then write the groups of words in the correct places.

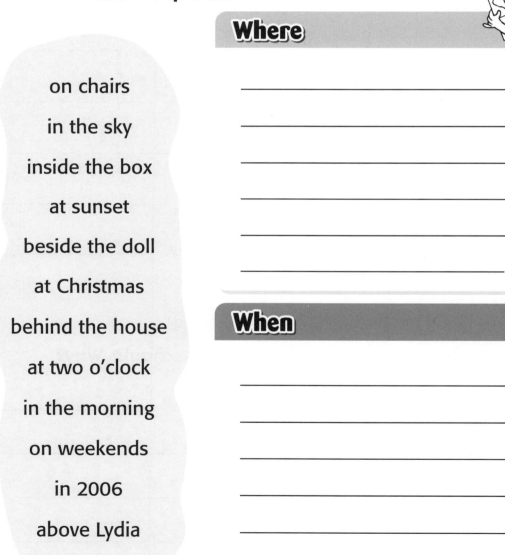

on chairs

in the sky

inside the box

at sunset

beside the doll

at Christmas

behind the house

at two o'clock

in the morning

on weekends

in 2006

above Lydia

Where

_____

_____

_____

_____

_____

_____

When

_____

_____

_____

_____

_____

_____

ISBN: 978-1-897164-31-0

D. Circle the correct prepositions to complete the sentences.

1. **At / On** my birthday last year, my parents held a party for me. They invited a clown to the party. The clown show started 2. **at / in** three o'clock. My friends and I sat 3. **in / on** the carpet to watch the performance.

The clown had a few balls of different colours 4. **in / inside** her hands. She juggled the balls and we were amazed to see that they formed a colourful arc 5. **above / in** the air.

The clown then took out a box the size of a small toaster oven from 6. **in / under** the table. She showed us that there was nothing 7. **between / inside** it. She put the box 8. **in / on** the middle of the table and said "Abracadabra". Then she slowly pulled a teddy bear out of the box. My friend Anson whispered to me that there must be a hidden part 9. **at / under** the bottom of the box. But the clown continued to pull teddy bears

out. Two, three, four... We all clapped loudly when she put the tenth teddy bear 10. **above / on** the table. How could she hide ten teddy bears 11. **in / beside** such a small box?

ISBN: 978-1-897164-31-0

My Brother Loves to Dance

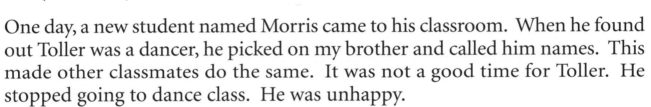

My brother Toller is a very good dancer. He is 12 years old and has been dancing for about six years. He has won many awards. He loves being a dancer, but it wasn't always this way.

One day, a new student named Morris came to his classroom. When he found out Toller was a dancer, he picked on my brother and called him names. This made other classmates do the same. It was not a good time for Toller. He stopped going to dance class. He was unhappy.

Toller's dance instructor came to visit. She wanted to know why Toller had stopped going to dance class. My parents and I were shocked; Toller hadn't told us he had stopped! We all sat together and talked it out. Toller explained that he was being teased at school. The instructor asked him what was making him sad. He was sad mainly because he wanted to dance.

We worked out a plan and role-played it together. My father pretended to be Morris. When he teased Toller about being a dancer, Toller replied, "Yes, I am a dancer. I'm good at it, too. You are good at teasing and bothering people. You need to find something else to do." It didn't take long before Toller finally told Morris what we all thought. The other classmates stopped copying Morris. Soon Morris didn't have many friends. He stopped bothering Toller.

Toller danced some hip hop for a talent show at school last week. Everyone cheered when he was done...even Morris. I am proud of my brother.

     ISBN: 978-1-897164-31-0

A. Circle the correct answers.

1. Toller has been dancing for about ___ years.

   A. twelve   B. six   C. two

2. Toller was ___ when Morris called him names.

   A. happy   B. shocked   C. sad

3. Toller's ___ visited the writer's family to see why Toller had stopped going to dance class.

   A. class teacher   B. principal   C. dance instructor

4. ___ was good at teasing others.

   A. Morris   B. Toller   C. The writer

5. Toller danced some ___ for his school talent show.

   A. samba   B. hip hop   C. tap-dance

B. Rewrite the sentences so that they become correct.

1. Toller hasn't won any awards.

   _____

2. The writer pretended to be Morris in the role play.

   _____

   _____

3. Everyone jeered when Toller finished his dance.

   _____

   _____

ISBN: 978-1-897164-31-0

Contractions

A **contraction** is a short way of writing two words. One or more letters are replaced with an apostrophe.

Examples: I am → I'm
           was not → wasn't

C.   Draw lines to match the words with their contractions.

1. did not   •   • shouldn't

2. I have   •   • doesn't

3. does not   •   • there's

4. there is   •   • didn't

5. she is   •   • we'll

6. we will   •   • she's

7. should not •   • he'd

8. he had   •   • I've

D.   Fill in the blanks with the contractions of the given words.

1. Toller (did not) _____ go to the dance class yesterday.

2. He (could not) _____ finish his homework.

3. He (had not) _____ missed any dance classes before.

4. (He will) _____ never miss his dance class again.

5. (He would) _____ like to be a professional dancer in the future.

ISBN: 978-1-897164-31-0

Abbreviations

An **abbreviation** is the shortened form of a word or words.

Examples: Doctor → Dr.
Tuesday → Tue.
Royal Canadian Mounted Police → RCMP

E.   Circle the correct abbreviations for the words.

1. Mister   Ms. / Mrs. / Mr.

2. kilometre   ki / km / kilo

3. Boulevard   Bl. / Bv. / Blvd.

4. November   Nov. / No. / Novem.

5. number   num. / no. / nb.

6. British Columbia   Br.Co. / B.Co. / B.C.

7. Mountain   Mt. / Mo. / Mot.

F.   Rewrite the sentences using abbreviations.

1. Toller will join a dance competition in October.

    _____

2. It will take place in a school on Berry Drive.

    _____

3. He will go on a trip to Prince Edward Island afterwards.

    _____

ISBN: 978-1-897164-31-0

Lacrosse
Canada's National Summer Sport

Lacrosse is the oldest game in North America. It has been played by the native people of North America for more than 500 years. The first game took place in 1840, and it soon became very popular. In 1859, the government of Canada named lacrosse Canada's national game. In 1994, lacrosse was given the title of Canada's national summer sport.

Lacrosse can be played indoors or outdoors. Women's field lacrosse is played with two teams of 12 players. Men's field lacrosse teams have ten players. The players must pass and catch a rubber ball using netted sticks, and try to score goals by hurling the ball into the other team's goal area.

In the men's game, contact between players is allowed, so protective gear such as helmets and padding is worn. Women's lacrosse does not permit such contact between players. It is based more on the skills of ball control and passing, like the original version of lacrosse.

In the 1930s, box lacrosse was created. There are six players on a team. Box lacrosse requires players to think fast and be quick. It is more popular than field lacrosse in Canada.

Another type of lacrosse called inter-lacrosse is a non-contact sport. It is popular with children and teenaged players.

Lacrosse is one of the fastest growing sports in Canada. Why not give it a try?

ISBN: 978-1-897164-31-0

A. Put the events in order. Write 1 to 4 on the lines.

_____ Lacrosse was named Canada's national summer sport.

_____ Lacrosse was named Canada's national game.

_____ Box lacrosse was created.

_____ The first game of lacrosse was played.

B. Write "T" for the true sentences and "F" for the false ones.

1. Lacrosse can only be played outdoors.   _____

2. There are 12 players on a men's team in field
   lacrosse.   _____

3. The players score goals by kicking the ball into
   the net.   _____

4. No contact between players is allowed in
   women's lacrosse.   _____

5. The original version of lacrosse is based on the
   skills of ball control and passing.   _____

6. Players in box lacrosse have to think fast and
   be quick.   _____

7. Field lacrosse is more popular than box lacrosse
   in Canada.   _____

8. Children can take part in inter-lacrosse.   _____

ISBN: 978-1-897164-31-0

Prefixes

A **prefix** is a group of letters added to the beginning of a word that changes the meaning of the word.

The prefix "re" means "to do again".
The prefix "un" means "not" or "opposite of".

Examples: write → <u>re</u>write

happy → <u>un</u>happy

C. Cross out ✗ the words that do not use "re" or "un" as a prefix.

 **Re**    **Un**

react	result
reach	rewind
retrieve	retake
repeat	rebuild
rename	restart

under	uncertain
unkind	uncover
unit	unstable
unless	uncle
unable	unseen

D. Add "re" or "un" to the given words to complete the sentences.

1. Field lacrosse is (popular) _____ in Southeast Asia.

2. The government is planning to (develop) _____ this district.

3. You have to (set) _____ your watch to local time.

4. I didn't see that part clearly. Can you (play) _____ it?

5. It is (wise) _____ to take action now.

ISBN: 978-1-897164-31-0

Suffixes

A **suffix** is a group of letters added to the end of a word that changes the meaning of the word.

The suffix "al" means "of" or "related to". The suffix "ful" means "full of". The suffix "less" means "without".

Examples: origin → origin<u>al</u>

meaning → meaning<u>ful</u>

meaning → meaning<u>less</u>

E. Read the clues and complete the crossword puzzle.

Across

A. full of joy
B. of a nation
C. without colour
D. of a region

Down

1. related to education
2. full of hope
3. without care

Rupinder the Reporter

Rupinder is a member of the newspaper club at his school. His club publishes a school newspaper once a month. Rupinder is a reporter for the paper. His job is to find things to write about. The students of his school like reading his articles.

This month, Rupinder wrote about his classmate, Toller. Toller has won many awards for his amazing dancing. He is famous in the city because he is such a good dancer. Rupinder's article focused on how hard Toller practised to become a good dancer.

Last month, Rupinder wrote a story about his school's "green program". His school has new hand dryers in the washrooms, so they don't use paper towels anymore. Also, they have recycling bins at school. No paper cups are allowed in the staff room or cafeteria anymore.

Right now, Rupinder is working on an article about bullying at school. He notices bullies like to keep things secret, but he is going to make sure it is not a secret anymore!

Rupinder loves his job on the school newspaper. When he grows up, he wants to be a famous journalist.

ISBN: 978-1-897164-31-0

A. Check ✔ the main idea of each paragraph.

Paragraph One

A   Rupinder is a reporter for his school newspaper.

B   There is a newspaper club at Rupinder's school.

Paragraph Two

A   Rupinder wrote about Toller this month.

B   Toller practised hard to become a good dancer.

Paragraph Three

A   No paper cups are allowed in Rupinder's school.

B   Rupinder wrote about his school's "green program" last month.

Paragraph Four

A   Bullies like to keep things secret.

B   Rupinder is working on an article about bullying at his school.

Paragraph Five

A   Rupinder wants to work for his school newspaper when he grows up.

B   Rupinder wants to be a famous journalist when he grows up.

ISBN: 978-1-897164-31-0

Compound Words

A **compound word** is formed when two words are put together to form a new word of a different meaning.

Example: news + paper = newspaper

B. **Unscramble the letters to form compound words. Circle the words in the word search.**

n a y + r o e m   w t e r a + l a f l   i a r n + w b o

t o f o + i n p r t   s h w a + o o r m   y e k + a d b r o

l u e b + a y j   a t e r f + o n n o   a s c l s + t a m e

c	s	m	a	t	c	p	a	m	y	m	o	t	h	c
l	o	o	f	j	v	r	i	n	t	l	g	c	b	i
a	p	j	t	a	w	a	t	e	r	f	a	l	l	w
s	c	k	e	y	x			h	a	o	m	a	u	a
e	l	o	r	w					o	a	s	e	t	
r	a	i	n	j					t	o	k	j	e	
g	s	m	o	t					p	e	e	a	n	
b	s	d	o	d					r	t	y	y	b	
n	m	v	n	l	n	w	s	r	a	i	n	b	o	w
w	a	s	h	r	o	o	m	j	p	n	l	o	k	n
a	t	e	r	n	o	f	a	q	e	t	h	a	b	z
k	e	y	b	j	n	r	a	n	y	m	o	r	e	f
g	d	k	a	s	c	i	t	r	e	b	k	d	i	a

ISBN: 978-1-897164-31-0

C. **Draw lines to match the pictures to form compound words. Write the words in the boxes.**

1.

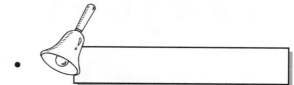

2.

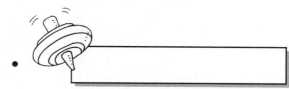

3.

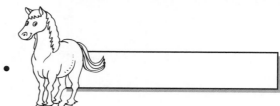

4.

5.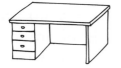

D. **Draw two pictures to form a compound word. Write the word on the line.**

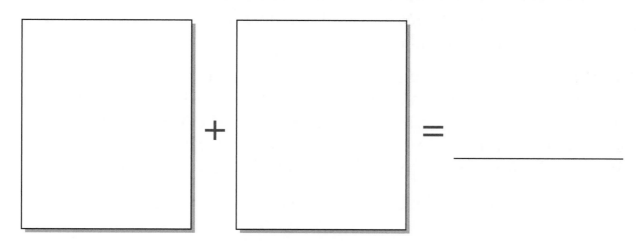

\+ = _____

ISBN: 978-1-897164-31-0

A Special Project

One day my mother asked me if I wanted to do a special crocheting project with my friends. I said yes. I invited four friends over for a pyjama party. I told them to bring their crochet hooks. My mother taught us how to make crocheted squares.

We started to crochet big squares. There were five of us, and we each made four squares. My mom had bought different colours of wool: peony pink, sky blue, buttercup yellow, lime green, and lavender. My mom made four squares, too.

Then my mom showed us how to sew four squares into a row. We made small, careful stitches using white wool. Then we sewed the six rows together. It turned into a large rainbow-coloured blanket. My mom took a photograph of all of us with our blanket.

That night, we all tried to sleep under the blanket, but it was a bit too small! The next morning, we took a bus to an orphanage. My mom said the children there don't have any parents. The lady who ran the orphanage was kind. We gave her the blanket we made and she thanked us. She took us to a playroom. We played with some of the babies for a little while. They were sweet.

We were glad to meet the babies and give them our blanket.

ISBN: 978-1-897164-31-0

A. Give short answers to the questions.

1. What did they need to make crocheted squares?

    _____

2. How many crocheted squares did they make?

    _____

3. What did they use to sew the squares together?

    _____

4. What did they make with the crocheted squares?

    _____

5. Where did they go the next day?

    _____

B. Crocheted squares can be sewn together to make different things. Write one thing that you would like to make with crocheted squares. Draw a picture to go with it.

    _____

Commonly Confused Words

We may confuse words that have similar spellings or sound alike.

Examples: bought – brought
sew – sow

C. Circle the correct words to complete the sentences.

1. My mom is crocheting a big
| circle |
| cycle |
.

2. She wants to make a
| vary |
| very |
big
| cloth |
| clothe |
to cover the table.

3. She puts the wool on the small table
| beside |
| besides |
the
| coach |
| couch |
.

4. Oh
| dear |
| deer |
! The stitches here are too
| lose |
| loose |
.

5. Adrian, could you
| pass |
| past |
the wool to me?

6.
| Its |
| It's |
very beautiful, Mom.

7. Mom likes having a
| desert |
| dessert |
after crocheting.

ISBN: 978-1-897164-31-0

D. The underlined words are wrong in the sentences. Write the correct words on the lines.

1. I think crocheting is <u>quiet</u> interesting. _____

2. Wait at the <u>curd</u> before crossing the road. _____

3. He <u>pores</u> the juice into a big jug. _____

4. I helped Mom <u>sat</u> the table. _____

5. This is a <u>nine-story</u> building. _____

6. Mrs. Hopewell is talking to the school <u>principle</u>. _____

7. Kim made a <u>bald</u> move in joining the contest. _____

8. The zebra has black and white <u>strips</u>. _____

E. Write sentences with the words to show the difference in meaning between the words in each pair.

1. diner / dinner

_____

_____

2. forth / fourth

_____

_____

Fruit is always a delicious treat. In Canada, we grow a lot of apples, pears, cherries, and cranberries. But Canada is too cold to grow certain fruits.

Have you ever tasted a durian? It is grown in warm places like Malaysia and Thailand in Southeast Asia. The name "durian" comes from the Malay word *duri*, meaning "thorn".

The durian is often called "King of the Fruits" because it is big and dangerous looking, and has a very strong smell. One durian can grow up to 40 centimetres long and 30 centimetres wide. It can weigh up to five kilograms. It is an oval shape and the outside is a hard, greenish-brown husk. It is covered with prickly thorns.

But the most amazing thing about the durian is what is inside. When you open it up, a very strong smell comes out. Some people love this smell but others hate it! In Singapore, you are not permitted to bring a durian into your hotel room or onto city trains. Some airlines will not let you carry a durian onto the airplane.

Durian
King of the Fruits

Despite the smell, the flesh inside is quite tasty. It is yellowish in colour, and tastes a little bit like custard. Forest animals such as squirrels, wild pigs, and orangutans love it.

KING
OF THE
FRUITS

ISBN: 978-1-897164-31-0

A. Write the words in the correct places.

cherries

Malaysia

cranberries

Thailand

Singapore

wild pigs

durians

squirrels

pears

orangutans

Canada

Fruit

_____

_____

_____

_____

Animal

_____

_____

_____

Place

_____

_____

_____

_____

B. Complete the chart.

The Durian

Shape: 1. _____   Weight: up to 2. _____ kg

Length: up to 3. _____ cm   Width: up to 4. _____ cm

Colour: husk – 5. _____ ; flesh – 6. _____

ISBN: 978-1-897164-31-0

Synonyms and Antonyms

Synonyms are words that have similar meanings.

Examples: cold – chilly

Antonyms are words that have opposite meanings.

Examples: cold – hot

C.   Circle the synonyms and underline the antonyms of the shaded words.

1. big

large

small

huge

2. love

hate

like

dislike

3. fast

speedy

slow

swift

4. delicious

yummy

tasty

flavourless

5. cloudy

overcast

sunny

bright

6. balmy

pleasant

warm

stormy

7. interesting

boring

absorbing

amusing

ISBN: 978-1-897164-31-0

D. Fill in the blanks with synonyms for the given words.

1. It is too (cold) _____ to grow durians in Canada.

2. We are planning a (holiday) _____ in Thailand.

3. Why is your room so (messy) _____ ?

4. This dish is too (spicy) _____ for me.

5. Don't bring a durian into this hotel. It is not (allowed) _____ .

6. The first train (departs) _____ at six thirty in the morning.

E. Rewrite the sentences with antonyms for the underlined words.

1. I seldom try exotic fruits.

   _____

2. This store opens on Sundays.

   _____

3. The old lady is choosing a small durian.

   _____

ISBN: 978-1-897164-31-0

The Story of Honey

Honey is made by bees. They make honey for wintertime when flowers are not blooming and nectar is not available. Lucky for us, there are so many bees to make honey that there is plenty for us, too.

Honeybees live and work together in colonies. A colony of honeybees includes a queen bee, drone bees, and worker bees. The queen is the largest bee in the colony, and she lays all the eggs for the colony. The drones help the queen make eggs.

Worker bees are the smallest bees. One colony can have as many as 60 000 worker bees. Their job is to collect nectar from flowers to make honey. They also make the honeycomb from beeswax to store the honey. Drones may live up to eight weeks and worker bees live about five to six weeks. A queen bee may live up to five years.

There are many kinds of honey and they taste different, depending on the flowers the bees take the nectar from. The average worker bee makes about 1/10 of a teaspoon of honey in its lifetime! A honeybee will visit 50 to 150 flowers on one trip. To make half a kilogram of honey the bees must tap two million flowers and fly over 40 kilometres. Half a kilogram of honey is what 300 bees can make in their lifetime!

It takes a lot of work to make honey. No wonder it tastes so good!

ISBN: 978-1-897164-31-0

A. Complete the chart.

A Honeybee Colony

Queen Bee

- the 1._____ bee
- Number: 2._____
- Job: 3._____
- Lifespan: up to 4._____

Drone Bee

- Job: 5._____
- Lifespan: 6._____

7._____

- the smallest bee
- Number: as many as 8._____
- Jobs: 9._____

  10._____

- Lifespan: 11._____

ISBN: 978-1-897164-31-0

Similes

A **simile** is a comparison of two things that have something in common. The two things are linked by "as" or "like".

Examples: He *is* hardworking *like* a worker bee.
These candies are *as* sweet *as* honey.

B. Check ✔ if the sentences use similes.

1. The city is as busy as a bee colony.

2. The honeycomb is like a storeroom.

3. The beehive is as big as a basketball.

4. My parents like to add honey to their coffee.

5. Little Sharon smiled as she tasted the honey.

6. Honey is as tasty as maple syrup.

7. Mr. Gibson works as a beekeeper.

8. Would you like to try some?

9. The flowers are colourful like a rainbow.

ISBN: 978-1-897164-31-0

C. Complete the similes with the given words.

a hotel   snails   a ball   birds   a stone   coffee

1. The full moon is as round as _____ .

2. The cars are moving slowly like _____ .

3. This chocolate is bitter like _____ .

4. The coconut is as hard as _____ .

5. Her house is as luxurious as

   _____ .

6. The children sing sweetly like

   _____ .

D. Rewrite the sentences using similes.

1. The little girl is beautiful.

   _____

2. This flashlight is bright.

   _____

3. The phone is ringing loudly.

   _____

ISBN: 978-1-897164-31-0

Hello around the World

In Canada, most people say *Hello* and *Bonjour* when we greet people. Have you ever wondered what people say in other countries? Japanese people will bow and say *Ohayo*. In China, they say *Ni hao*. In Thailand, *Sawatdee* is said. In Korea, they say *Anyong haseyo*. In Africa, *Jambo* is the Swahili word for "Hello".

People in Egypt, Iraq, Syria, Qatar, and Oman greet each other by saying *Salam* which is an Arabic word. Many languages are spoken in India, but in Hindi – one of the most common languages there – people say *Namaste*. In Malaysia and Indonesia, people say *Apa kabar*.

There are a lot of countries in Europe, and a lot of languages, too! In Italy, people say *Bongiorno* (which means "good day"). In Denmark people say *Goddag*, and in the Netherlands people say *Goede dag*. In Spain, Mexico, and Cuba, people speak Spanish. They say *Hola*. In Germany people say *Guten tag* (good day) or *Hallo*. Over in Russia, people say *Privyet*.

In Hawaii, people say *Aloha*, which means hello, goodbye, and love. In Israel, people speak Hebrew. When people greet each other there, they say *Shalom*. It means hello, goodbye, and peace.

It is fun to greet people in their own first language. Why not give it a try?

ISBN: 978-1-897164-31-0

A. Draw lines to match the greetings with the countries.

Africa •

China •

Israel •

Thailand •

Canada •

Germany •

Japan •

Hawaii •

Korea •

India •

Spain •

Italy •

• Ohayo

• Aloha

• Jambo

• Bonjour

• Ni hao

• Hola

• Hallo

• Hello

• Bongiorno

• Anyong haseyo

• Guten tag

• Shalom

• Namaste

• Sawatdee

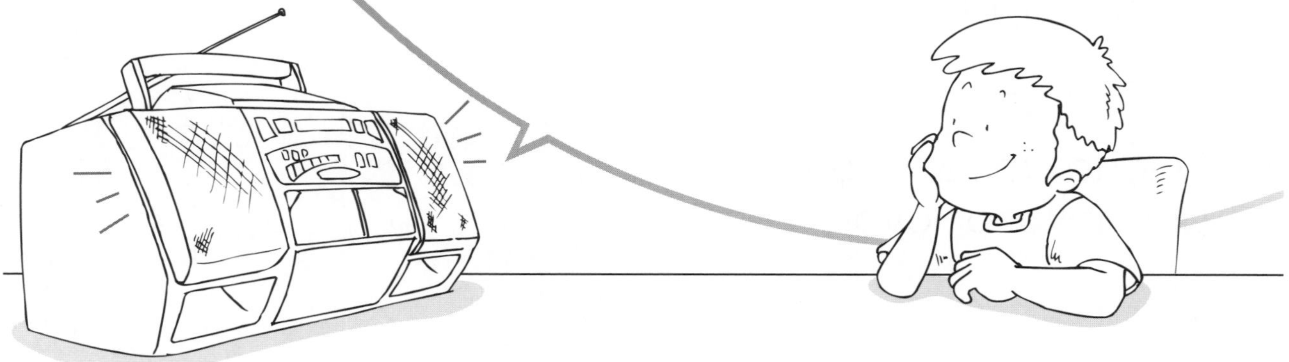

ISBN: 978-1-897164-31-0

Conjunctions

A **conjunction** like "and", "or", or "but" can be used to join words or sentences.

Example: In Canada, some people say "Hello". Others say "Bonjour".

In Canada, some people say "Hello" <u>and</u> others say "Bonjour".

B. Check ✔ if the underlined words are correct. Otherwise, correct the wrong ones and write them on the lines.

1. My sister is fluent in Spanish <u>or</u> I just know a little Spanish.   _____

2. We can either learn the language ourselves <u>and</u> take a course on it.   _____

3. The tourist kept speaking Japanese <u>and</u> I did not understand what he was saying.   _____

4. You can watch the English version <u>or</u> the French version of the film.   _____

5. Macy wants to learn a language <u>and</u> she hasn't decided which one to learn.   _____

6. "Hello", "Hola", <u>and</u> "Hallo" sound similar.

   _____

7. "Aloha" means hello, goodbye, <u>or</u> love.

   _____

Aloha!

Hello!

ISBN: 978-1-897164-31-0

C. Fill in the blanks with "and", "or", or "but".

1. Who is your class teacher this year, Miss Sheldon _____ Mrs. Winsor?

2. This computer is old _____ it still functions well.

3. You can stay here _____ come with me.

4. Toronto is a big city _____ there are lots of high-rise buildings in downtown Toronto.

5. This storybook is interesting _____ it is full of colourful pictures too.

6. Ray wants to fly his kite _____ there is no wind.

D. Join the sentences using "and", "or", or "but".

1. I wanted to call Tracy. Her line was busy.

   _____

   _____

2. I'll get some snacks. You'll prepare the drinks.

   _____

   _____

3. Put your shoes in the box. Leave them on the rug.

   _____

   _____

ISBN: 978-1-897164-31-0

My Brother, the Babysitter

My big brother Colin is a babysitter. He is 15 years old. He always looks after me, and now he looks after my friends and classmates too.

Colin likes his job. He tries very <u>hard</u> to be a good babysitter. Last year, he took <u>special</u> classes at a babysitter school. He learned many important things there. He learned to ask the parents a lot of questions before they went out, like "Where are you going?", "When will you be <u>back</u>?", and "What is your cellphone number?" He also asks about fire exits and fire meeting <u>points</u>. Sometimes the parents don't know the answers so they make the rules together.

Colin keeps a list of all the important phone numbers, such as the numbers of the police department, the fire department, the family doctor, and another adult who lives nearby.

Colin knows how to help someone stop choking. He also knows what to do if someone gets cut or burned. He doesn't use the oven when he is babysitting.

The best thing Colin does when he is babysitting me is that he plays with me! His head is filled with ideas about fun things to do. My friends tell me that my brother is a great babysitter. I think so too.

ISBN: 978-1-897164-31-0

A. Check ✔ the correct meanings of the underlined words as they are used in the passage.

1. special   A   not common

   B   designed for a particular purpose

2. back   A   rear part of something

   B   return

3. hard   A   with great effort

   B   not soft

4. points   A   places

   B   marks

B. Answer the following questions.

1. How can you tell that Colin tries very hard to be a good babysitter?

   _____

2. Write one question that Colin will ask the parents.

   _____

3. Why doesn't Colin use the oven when he is babysitting? Give your opinion.

   _____

   _____

ISBN: 978-1-897164-31-0

Forming Questions (1)

We can use "do", "does", "is", or "are" or their past form to begin a question.

Examples: <u>Is</u> your brother a babysitter too?

<u>Did</u> he take special classes in babysitting?

C. Fill in the blanks with the correct words to form questions.

do   does   did   is

are   was   were

1. _____ your sister look after you when your parents are not at home?

2. _____ the children need babysitting?

3. _____ Sara good at looking after children?

4. _____ his parents there when you arrived at his place?

5. _____ you interested in learning to be a babysitter?

6. _____ you do well in last year's babysitting course?

7. _____ Carla five when you started babysitting her?

ISBN: 978-1-897164-31-0

Forming Questions (2)

Words like "what", "when", "where", "which", "who", "why", and "how" can also be used in asking questions.

Examples: <u>Who</u> is Amy's family doctor?

<u>Which</u> number should I call first?

D. You will be babysitting Billy. Write the questions that you will ask his parents with the given words.

1. What

2. When

3. Where

4. Why

5. How

Most mammals, like dogs and whales, and people too, give birth to living babies. When the babies are born, they drink milk from the mother's body and grow quickly.

But marsupials are a unique kind of mammals. They are sometimes called "pouched mammals". This is because the mother has a pouch somewhere on her body. Marsupial babies are born differently from most other mammals. When they are born, they are still very tiny and unformed. They are born blind and hairless. The tiny marsupial baby must crawl through its mother's fur to find the pouch. It is a dangerous journey.

Once the baby finds the pouch, it will stay there and drink milk until it is big and strong enough to live as a real baby animal. It will start to explore the world, but go back into its mother's pouch when it wants to. The young marsupial will continue to drink its mother's milk for a long time – even when it has become too big to fit in its mother's cozy pouch!

Marsupials

There are many kinds of marsupials, but most of them live in Australia. Kangaroos, koalas, and wombats are the most familiar kinds of marsupials. There is only one kind of marsupial living in North America. It is called the opossum. They live mostly in forested areas and prairie grasslands. They are about the size of a cat. They hunt mostly at night, looking for small rodents, as well as insects, worms, fruits, seeds, and nuts.

ISBN: 978-1-897164-31-0

A.   Put the sentences in order. Write 1 to 5.

____ The baby stays in the pouch.

____ A baby marsupial is born.

____ The baby finds its mother's pouch.

____ The baby goes out to explore the world.

____ The baby gets back to its mother's pouch.

B.   Rewrite the sentences so that they become correct.

1.   Marsupial babies are born blind with lots of hair.

_____

_____

2.   The baby has to find its father's pouch on its own.

_____

_____

3.   Most marsupials live in North America.

_____

_____

4.   The opossum is about the size of a kangaroo.

_____

_____

ISBN: 978-1-897164-31-0

Paragraphs

A **paragraph** is a group of sentences that express the same idea.

A good paragraph has a **topic sentence** which is usually the first sentence and introduces the main idea, and **supporting sentences** that add details to that idea.

C. **Put a line through the sentence that does not belong in each paragraph in the passage below.**

The Opossum

The opossum is a marsupial. The mother has a pouch, like a kangaroo. You cannot find other kinds of marsupials in Canada. It has a triangular head and a pointed nose. Its fur is grey, but its ears and tail are furless. It can hang from a tree limb on its long tail.

The opossum is a mammal. The mother gives birth to living babies. The opossum baby is very tiny when it is born. It is just the size of a honeybee. Honeybees are hardworking insects. It climbs up its mother's fur to the pouch. It stays there for about 60 days. Then it will be strong enough to leave the pouch to see the world outside.

Opossums eat a wide variety of things. They like looking for food at night. They eat worms, snails, insects, and small animals like rodents. A spider is not an insect. They also eat seeds, fruits, and nuts of different plants. Even pet food can be their food.

ISBN: 978-1-897164-31-0

D. Write a topic sentence for each paragraph below.

1. _____

I knew her when I was four. She was my neighbour and we were in the same kindergarten class. Although her family has moved, we still meet each other often. I tell her my little secrets and she shares hers with me. We'll stay best friends forever.

2. _____

You can find it on the Canadian flag. It has been on the penny since 1937. Many tourists to Canada like to buy souvenirs with the maple leaf on them. People around the world will surely think of Canada when they see a maple leaf.

3. _____

My alarm clock didn't work so I got up late. I missed the school bus and had to take the bus to school. On the way, the bus broke down. It was just two blocks away from school so I decided to walk the remaining distance. When I was near school, it suddenly rained heavily. I was soaked to the skin. To make matters worse, I found that I had left my bag on the bus. It was probably the worst day in my life.

ISBN: 978-1-897164-31-0

A. Fill in the blanks with the correct verb form to complete the sentences about the panda family.

Mother Panda and Father Panda (have) 1._____ given birth to a baby panda. It (be) 2._____ a girl. They (call) 3._____ her Pui Pui.

Pui Pui (be) 4._____ pink and very small. She (be) 5._____ just about the size of a chipmunk. She (do) 6._____ not look like her mom or dad at all.

Friends of the family (come) 7._____ to visit them. They (be) 8._____ all happy to meet Pui Pui for the first time. They (have) 9._____ brought some bamboo shoots as gifts for Pui Pui.

Mother Panda (smile) 10._____ and (remind) 11._____ them that Pui Pui (be) 12._____ still too young to eat bamboo shoots. They all (laugh) 13._____ together.

ISBN: 978-1-897164-31-0

B. **Pui Pui is now one year old. She is very different from the time when she was born. Add the given adjectives or adverbs in the correct places to tell about her.**

1. Pui Pui's body is covered with fur. (thick) (white)

   _____

   _____

   _____

2. She has eye patches, ears, legs, and shoulders. (black)

   _____

   _____

3. She likes eating bamboo leaves and shoots. (fresh)

   _____

   _____

4. She eats to stay healthy. (fast)

   _____

5. She likes to walk in the forest. (slowly)

   _____

6. She can climb trees. (easily)

   _____

C. Pui Pui made a friend in the forest. Fill in the blanks with the prepositions and the correct form of the verbs.

on	in	in	above	under
say	stand	walk	look	be	hope
become	see	come	get	hear

Pui Pui 1._____ around 2._____ the forest one day. She 3._____ sad because she does not have any brothers or sisters. She 4._____ that there would be someone to play with her.

She 5._____ 6._____ a tree kicking the grass 7._____ the ground aimlessly. Suddenly she 8._____ some laughter in the distance. It 9._____ closer and closer. Then a "hello" 10._____ from 11._____ her. She 12._____ up and 13._____ a monkey 14._____ the tree.

"Hi, my name is Kin Kin. Let's play together," 15._____ the monkey.

From that day onwards, the two of them 16._____ friends.

ISBN: 978-1-897164-31-0

D. Pui Pui and Kin Kin are playing. Read the clues and help them complete the crossword puzzle.

Across

A. not even
B. synonym of "beautiful"
C. antonym of "remember"
D. without harm
E. abbreviation of "centimetre"
F. full spelling of "Aug"

G. +

H. + //

Down

1. synonym of "packed"
2. antonym of "dangerous"
3. contraction of "should not"
4. contraction of "there is"
5. full of power
6. use again
7. related to tides

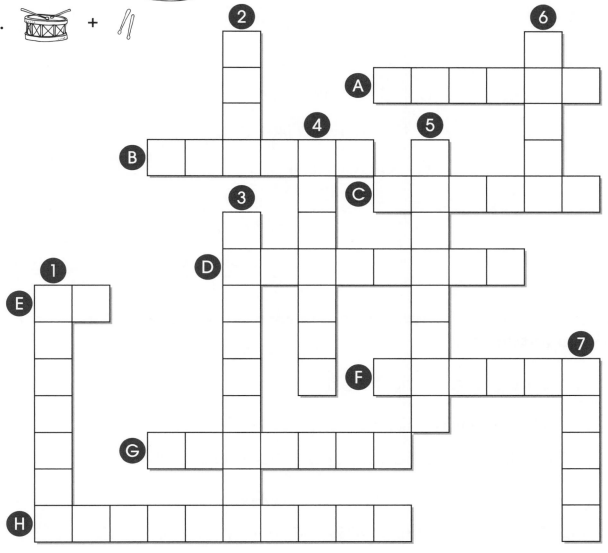

E. Help Pui Pui get to Kin Kin by completing the similes with the correct words.

desert	fly	peach	sea
seed	swan	ice	cheetah

1. as cold as _____

2. as fast as a _____

3. as dry as a _____

4. as tiny as a _____

5. pink like a _____

6. deep like the _____

7. annoying like a _____

8. graceful like a _____

F. Pui Pui has used a wrong word in each sentence. Help Kin Kin correct her mistakes.

1. It's very <u>quite</u> in the forest. _____

2. Do you want to have <u>diner</u> with me? _____

3. What <u>desert</u> would you like after the meal? _____

4. Bamboo shoots are <u>vary</u> delicious. _____

5. I don't want to walk <u>pass</u> the valley. _____

ISBN: 978-1-897164-31-0

G. Pui Pui is chatting with Kin Kin. Write her questions.

1. _____

   No, I don't like bamboo shoots.

2. _____

   I like to eat bananas.

3. _____

   I like bananas because they are sweet.

4. _____

   Yes, there are lots of bananas in this forest.

5. _____

   I eat bananas whenever I'm hungry.

6. _____

   I also like eating pears.

7. _____

   I like eating bananas better.

ISBN: 978-1-897164-31-0

ISBN: 978-1-897164-31-0

Aboriginal Peoples

Aboriginal peoples have lived for thousands of years on the land we now call Canada. When Europeans came to settle in the land, there were two big groups: **Iroquoians** and **Algonquians**.

A. There were smaller Aboriginal groups in each of the two big groups. Finish their names with the given words.

Neutral	Petun	Wendat
Haudenosaunee	Abenaki	Ojibway
Algonquin	Ottawa	Nipissing

Iroquoians

N_____

A_____

O_____

O_____

A_____

N_____

W_____

P_____

H_____

Algonquians

ISBN: 978-1-897164-31-0

B. **Read what this European says and look at the maps. Then write the correct letters to tell where Aboriginal peoples lived.**

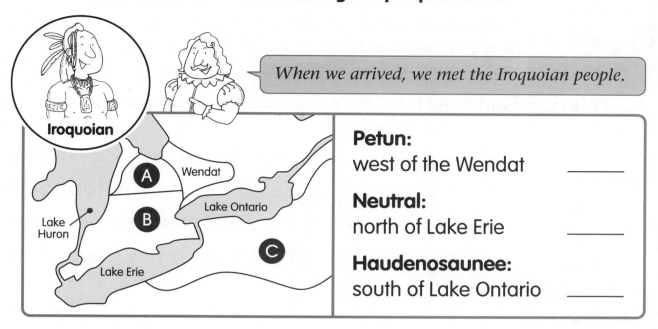

When we arrived, we met the Iroquoian people.

Petun:
west of the Wendat _____

Neutral:
north of Lake Erie _____

Haudenosaunee:
south of Lake Ontario _____

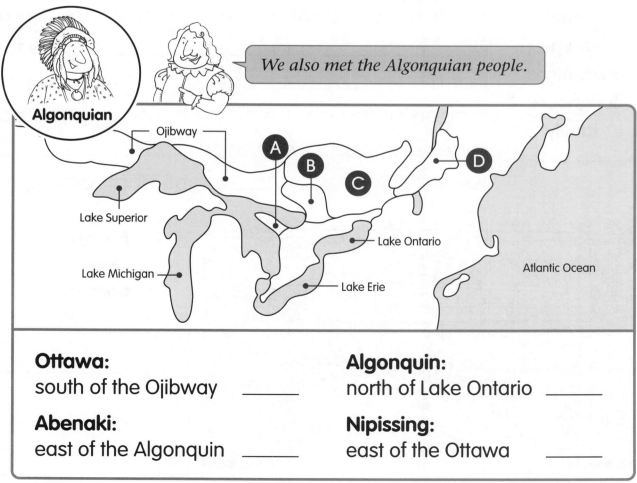

We also met the Algonquian people.

Ottawa:
south of the Ojibway _____

Algonquin:
north of Lake Ontario _____

Abenaki:
east of the Algonquin _____

Nipissing:
east of the Ottawa _____

ISBN: 978-1-897164-31-0

2

Houses of Aboriginal Peoples

The Iroquoians and Algonquians had different ways of life, so the houses that they built were different too.

A. Fill in the blanks and label the picture with the given words.

clan
beds
fires
hearths
village
warmth
storage
Iroquoians
longhouse
family

The 1._____ lived in villages close to their farmland. A 2._____ , the Iroquoian home, was shared by families of the same 3._____ . There were many longhouses in one 4._____ .

Inside the Iroquoian longhouse, there were 5._____ and 6._____ space for each 7._____ . 8._____ were placed at the centre of the house and shared by everyone. These indoor 9._____ were for 10._____ , light, and cooking.

hearth
bed
storage

11._____

12._____

13._____

ISBN: 978-1-897164-31-0

B. **Read what this Algonquian says. Circle "T" for the true sentences and "F" for the false ones. Then put the pictures in order. Write 1 to 4.**

> *We're not farmers like the Iroquoians. We hunt, trap, and fish for our food. We need homes that are easy and quick to build so that we can follow the animals as they migrate. Our homes are called "wigwams".*

1. The Algonquians were farmers.   T   F

2. The Algonquians did not fish.   T   F

3. Wigwams were easy to build.   T   F

4. The Algonquians moved very often.   T   F

5.

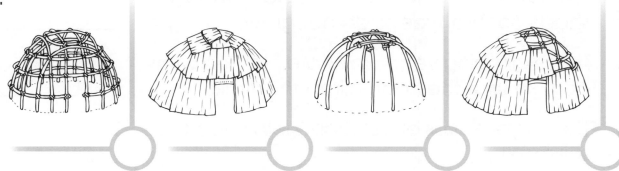

ISBN: 978-1-897164-31-0

What Aboriginal Peoples Ate

The Iroquoians and the Algonquians ate different types of food. The Iroquoians grew **corn**, **beans**, and **squash**. The Algonquians mainly **hunted**, **trapped**, and **fished** for their food.

A. **Look at the picture and read about what the Iroquoians ate. Then write the correct words in bold on the lines.**

Corn, beans, and squash were important to the Iroquoian people. These vegetables were planted together in small mounds of soil. The Iroquoian people called them the "Three Sisters".

1. This tall plant provides poles for beans to climb. _____

2. The leaves of this plant provide enough shade so that weeds do not grow. _____

3. These climbing vegetables are planted with corn so that they can climb the stalks. _____

4. The large leaves of this plant help keep the soil moist. _____

ISBN: 978-1-897164-31-0

B. **Look at these Algonquian tools. Write the correct letters on the lines to show what they were used for.**

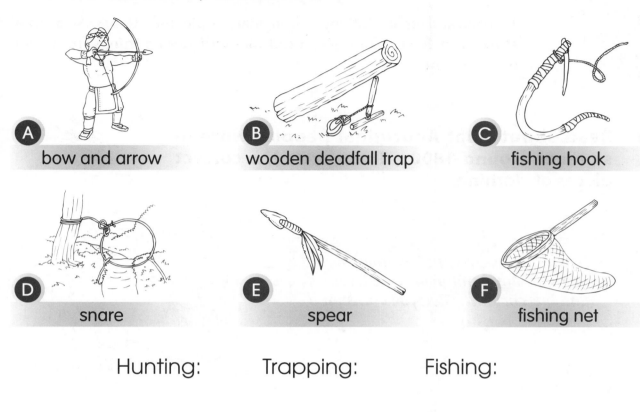

A bow and arrow

B wooden deadfall trap

C fishing hook

D snare

E spear

F fishing net

Hunting: Trapping: Fishing:

_____ _____ _____

C. **Look at these animal tracks. Match them with the correct animal names to see what the Algonquians hunted and trapped.**

beaver   moose   rabbit   wolf

1. _____

2. _____

3. _____

4. _____

ISBN: 978-1-897164-31-0

What Aboriginal Peoples Wore

To make and repair clothing, Aboriginal peoples used things like **animal skins** and **furs**. They also used many different things from their environment.

A. Read about what Aboriginal peoples wore in summer around 1800. Then circle the correct pieces of clothing.

> *In summer, girls and women wear dresses. Boys and men wear leggings and breechcloths. Everyone puts on a pair of moccasins.*

For men:

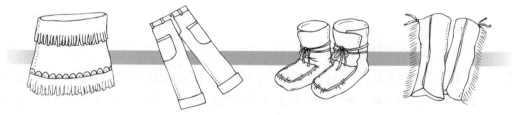

For women:

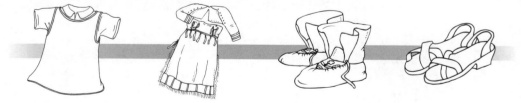

For children:

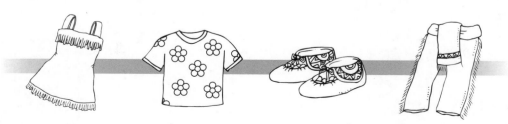

ISBN: 978-1-897164-31-0

B. Write "skin" or "fur" to tell what each moccasin is made with. Then draw lines to match the pairs.

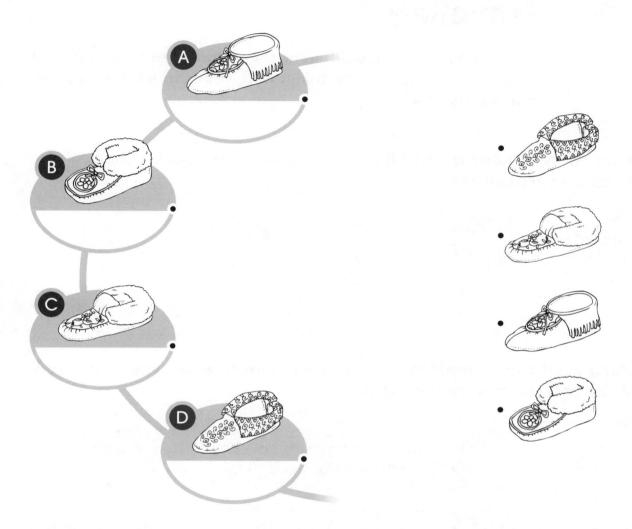

C. See if you know what each material was used for.

cloth   needle   weaving   thread

1. sinew _____   2. moose hair _____

3. roots _____   4. bone awls _____

5. deer skin _____   6. porcupine quills _____

ISBN: 978-1-897164-31-0

How Aboriginal Peoples Travelled

Aboriginal peoples had different things for travel to fit different conditions. Some of these things were **snowshoes**, **toboggans**, **canoes**, and **sleds**.

A. Canoes were made from hollowed-out logs or tree bark. Check ✔ the ones that are canoes.

B. Read what these children say and help them choose what they need. Write their names for the pictures.

Ben

We follow the migrating animals that provide us with food. We must travel many lakes and rivers.

Ada

Deep snow can't stop our hunt. We need something to be light on the snow for easy travelling.

Tom

We can't carry everything on our backs when we travel over snow and frozen lakes. We need something with room to carry our things.

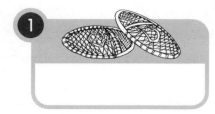

1

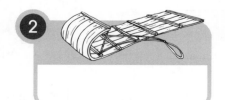

2

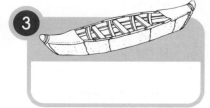

3

ISBN: 978-1-897164-31-0

C. **Help Alan, Kim, and Sara get to the party. Look how each of them travels. Then colour the correct pictures to find their paths. Use a different colour for each path.**

How Aboriginal Peoples Used Corn

Aboriginal peoples made many things from the corn plant. Different Aboriginal groups ground their corn differently. The Wendat people ground it in **hollowed-out logs**.

A. Which part of the corn plant is used to make each item? Write the correct letters.

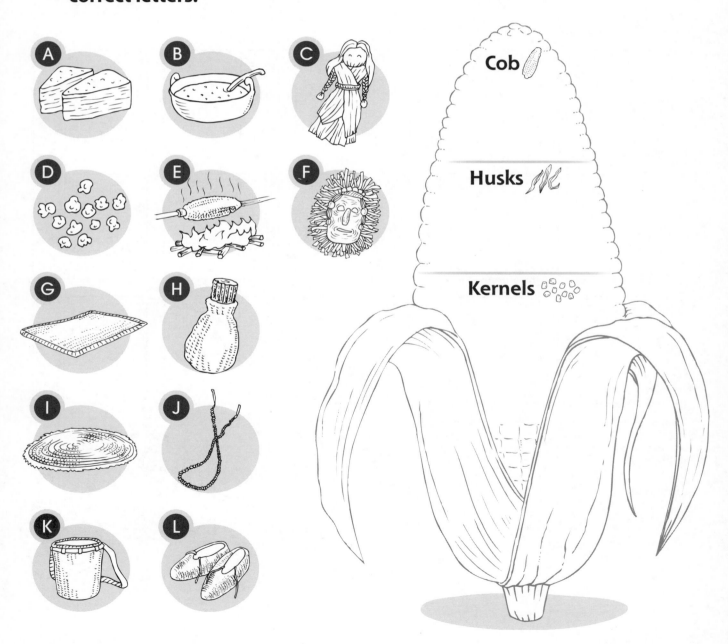

ISBN: 978-1-897164-31-0

B. Circle in the word search the names of things made from corn. Then fill in the blanks with the shaded letters to finish what Miss Corn says.

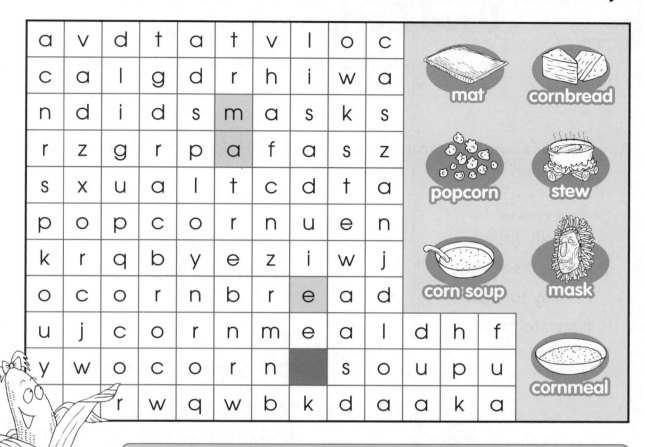

a	v	d	t	a	t	v	l	o	c
c	a	l	g	d	r	h	i	w	a
n	d	i	d	s	m	a	s	k	s
r	z	g	r	p	a	f	a	s	z
s	x	u	a	l	t	c	d	t	a
p	o	p	c	o	r	n	u	e	n
k	r	q	b	y	e	z	i	w	j
o	c	o	r	n	b	r	e	a	d
u	j	c	o	r	n	m	e	a	l	d	h	f
y	w	o	c	o	r	n		s	o	u	p	u
	r	w	q	w	b	k	d	a	a	k	a

mat   cornbread
popcorn   stew
corn soup   mask
cornmeal

You can also call me ___ ___ iz ___ . It's another word for corn.

C. Put the pictures in order to show how to hollow out a log for grinding corn. Write 1 to 4.

ISBN: 978-1-897164-31-0

How Aboriginal Peoples Used Bark

Tree bark has many qualities, so it was very useful to Aboriginal peoples.

A. **Susan is singing about the use of bark. Help her finish the verses with the given lines.**

Is easily found
Because it's strong
It's easy to twist
It's waterproof

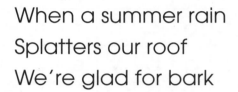

When a summer rain
Splatters our roof
We're glad for bark

1. _____

Our canoes must hold out
On trips far and long
They're made from birchbark

2. _____

Bark ropes and bark baskets
Are on my list
I use bark because

3. _____

We strip it from tree trunks
We find some on the ground
Elm bark or birchbark

4. _____

ISBN: 978-1-897164-31-0

B. Check ✔ the things made from bark.

1 canoe ☐

2 fishing hook ☐

3 container ☐

4 moose call ☐

5 basket ☐

6 drum ☐

7 fur pelt ☐

8 bone needle ☐

9 longhouse cover ☐

10 moccasins ☐

11 spearhead ☐

12 wigwam cover ☐

ISBN: 978-1-897164-31-0

Immigrants from Other Countries

Long ago, Canada was already a country of immigrants. These people came from many different places. They left their homeland for different reasons.

A. **Look at the map. Label it with the nationalities of the immigrants. Then fill in the blanks with the given words.**

A. American
B. British
C. Scottish
D. Irish
E. German

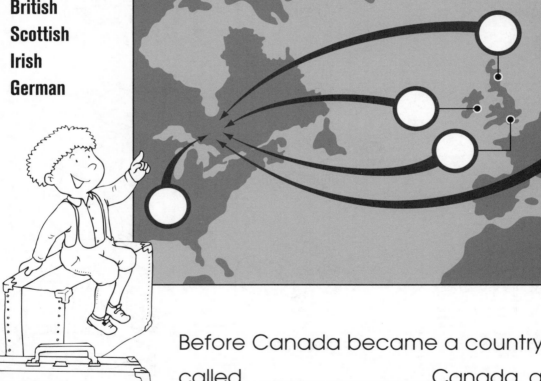

Europe

Ontario

immigrated

Upper

Before Canada became a country, it was called _____ Canada, and was made up only of _____ . Many people from _____ and the United States _____ here to make it their new home.

ISBN: 978-1-897164-31-0

B. **Read about the immigrants' reasons for coming to Canada. Then write the correct reason for each nationality of immigrants.**

There were many reasons people left their homeland for Canada. In Germany and the United States, some people were not free to practise their religion. Also in the United States, people who supported the British in a recent war were not allowed the same freedom as those who supported the Americans. In Britain, Ireland, and Scotland, there were too many people but not enough jobs and not enough land. There had also been years of bad potato crops. Many people were hungry.

Reasons

food

jobs

land

freedom of religion

equal freedom

German:

_____

American:

_____

_____

British, Scottish, Irish:

_____

_____

_____

ISBN: 978-1-897164-31-0

Journey of the Immigrants

People were encouraged to come to Canada. There were problems during the long journey, but there were also new things to see.

A.   Draw a poster that encourages people to come to Canada.

Don't forget to give your poster a title.

Make Canada Your Home!

ISBN: 978-1-897164-31-0

B.   Check ✔ the correct pictures in each group.

1.   Ways of coming to Canada:

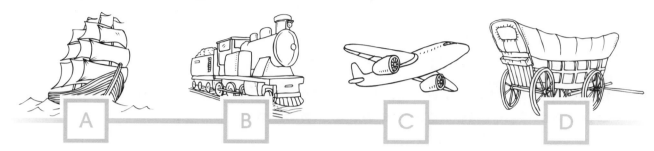

2.   Problems during the long travels:

3.   New sights during the travels:

4.   Tools for getting to Canada:

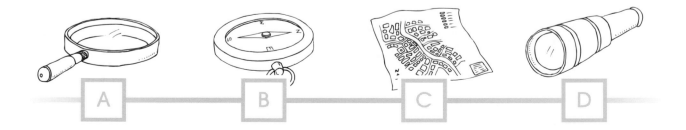

ISBN: 978-1-897164-31-0

The New Land

The immigrants were given new land and supplies to start their new lives in Canada. From there, they built their new homes and planted much of their own food.

A. **Read about the things given to the immigrants. Then complete the crossword puzzle with the words in bold.**

When the immigrants arrived in Canada, they were given a piece of **land** *and supplies for a good start. For example, they were given an* **axe** *and a* **hoe** *to clear the land,* **seeds** *for growing crops, a* **cow** *and a* **horse** *for the farm, and* **pork** *and* **flour** *for food. They were also given some* **clothes** *and* **money**.*

ISBN: 978-1-897164-31-0

B. Read what this immigrant says. Then put the pictures in order. Write 1 to 5.

There was a lot of work to do with the new land. First, we had to clear it. Then, we planted seeds around the stumps and saved the logs for building a house. In spring, we harvested our crops. Finally, we were able to enjoy the food we grew.

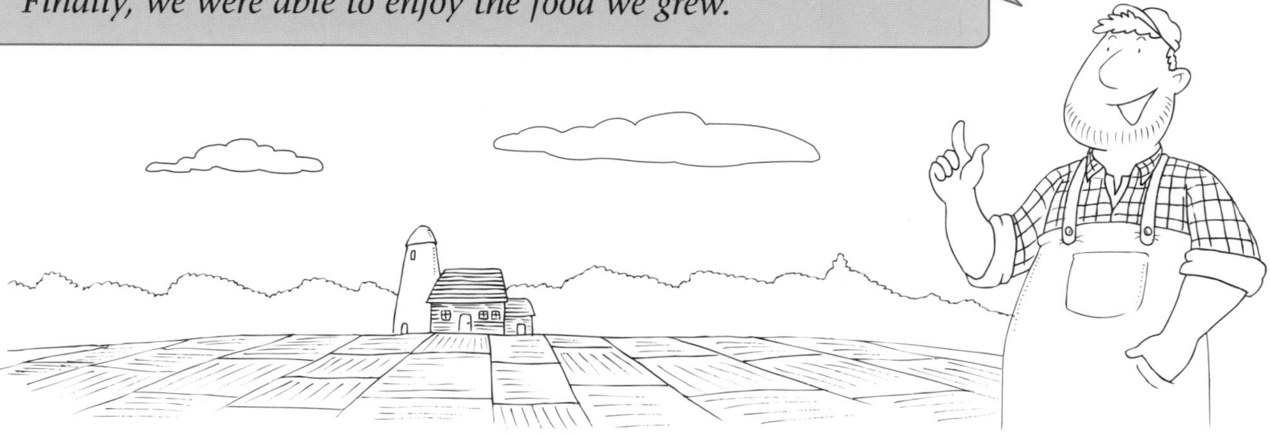

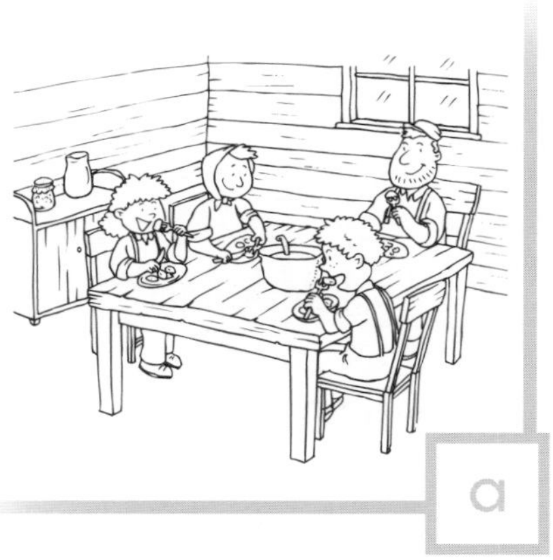

a

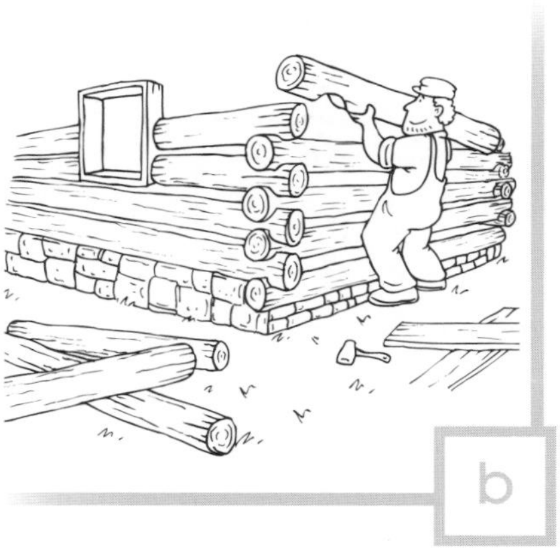

b

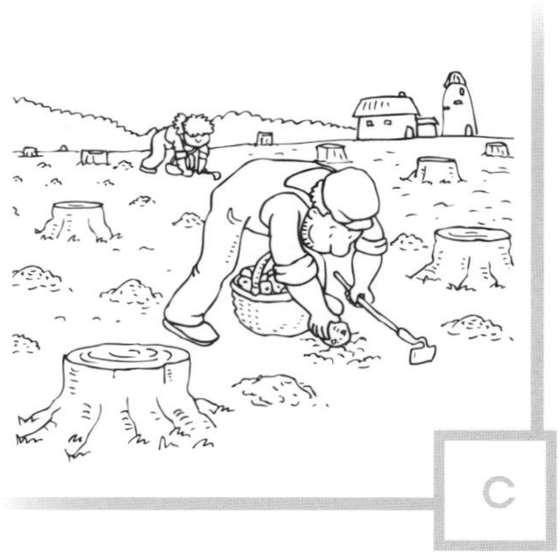

c

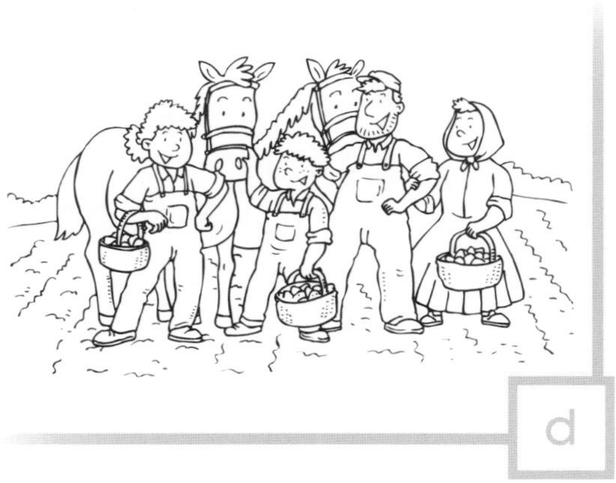

d

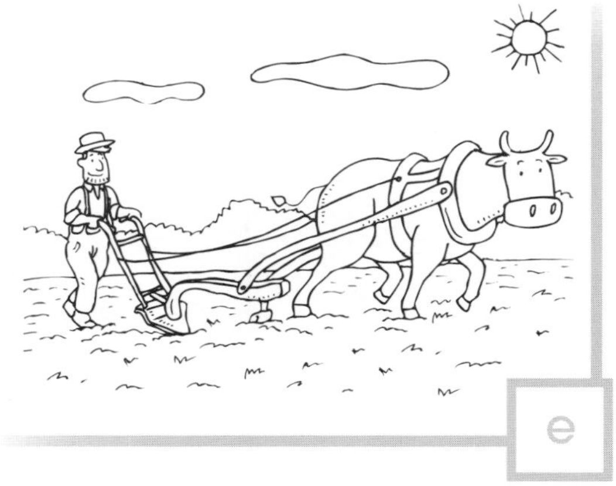

e

11

Jobs of the Settlers

The immigrants became settlers once they built a **settlement**, which needed different people for different jobs. The settlers had to do a lot of work. Even children had chores every day.

A. Read what the settlers say. Then draw lines to match the tools with the workers.

> We are all working to build a community on the new land. Each of us works with different things to do our jobs.

- blacksmith

- teacher

- miller

- sawyer

- merchant

- wagon maker

ISBN: 978-1-897164-31-0

B. **Look at the pictures. Fill in the blanks with the given words to tell what chores were done by the settlers.**

feed	cook	plant	make
harvest	wash	butcher	milk

1. Men's chores:

   _____ crops

   _____ crops

   _____ livestock

2. Women's chores:

   _____ meals

   _____ cows

   _____ clothes

   _____ crops

3. Children's chores:

   _____ chickens

   _____ dishes

ISBN: 978-1-897164-31-0

12

Food of the Settlers

The settlers **grew** plants and **raised** animals as food sources. They also **hunted** and **foraged** for food in the wild.

A. **Look at the pictures. Write the missing letters to tell what plants the settlers grew. Then draw lines to match the animals with the food items.**

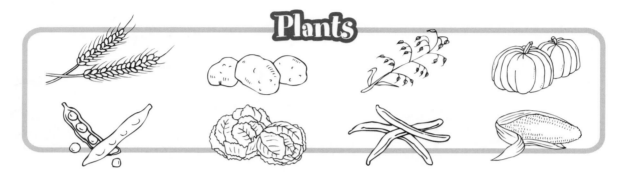

Plants

1. __ __rn

2. __hea__

3. c__ __b__ __e

4. p__ __s

5. b__ __ns

6. p__t__ __ __es

7. oa__ __

8. pum__ __ins

Animals

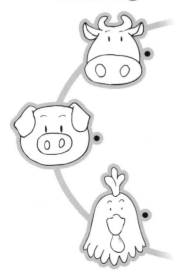

- drumsticks

- pork pie

- ham

- beef stew

- cheese

- milk

- eggs

ISBN: 978-1-897164-31-0

B. **Complete the crossword puzzle to tell what food the settlers found in the wild.**

Across

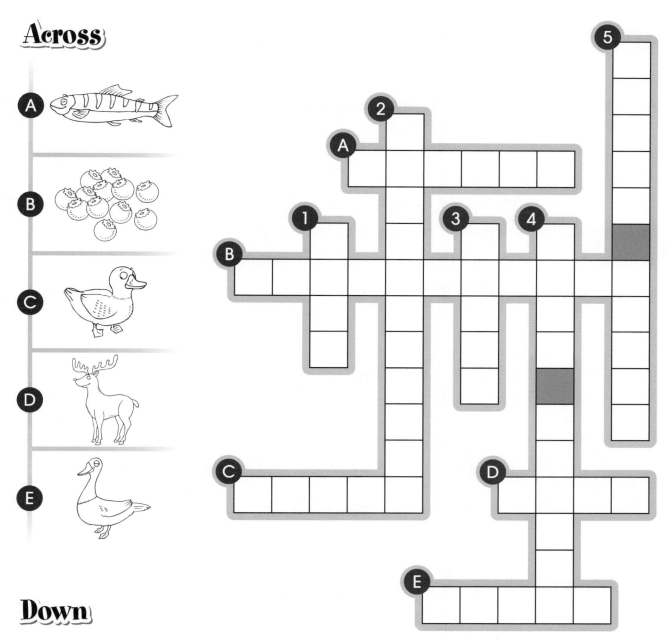

Down

1. what squirrels love
2. red berries
3. a kind of fish; rhymes with "about"
4. wild, green vegetables
5. sweet liquid from maple trees

ISBN: 978-1-897164-31-0

Grinding Grain

Every settlers' village had a **grist mill**. It was where different types of grain were ground into meal or flour.

A. **How did the grist mill compare with the old way of using a hollowed-out log? Circle the correct words.**

The grist mill was where a miller ground the farmers' grain quickly and easily. A waterwheel provided the energy for the mill to run all day. Before the settlers built a mill in the village, they ground their grain with a round stone or in a hollowed-out log, which could be located anywhere. The job could be done by anyone, but it took a very long time.

Grist Mill

1. **Power source:** human / water

   Location: near water / anywhere

   Worker: anyone / miller

   Time: long / short

Hollowed-out Log

2. **Power source:** human / water

   Location: near water / anywhere

   Worker: anyone / miller

   Time: long / short

ISBN: 978-1-897164-31-0

B. Unscramble the letters to find out what kinds of grain were ground at the grist mill. Then circle the food items made from meal or flour.

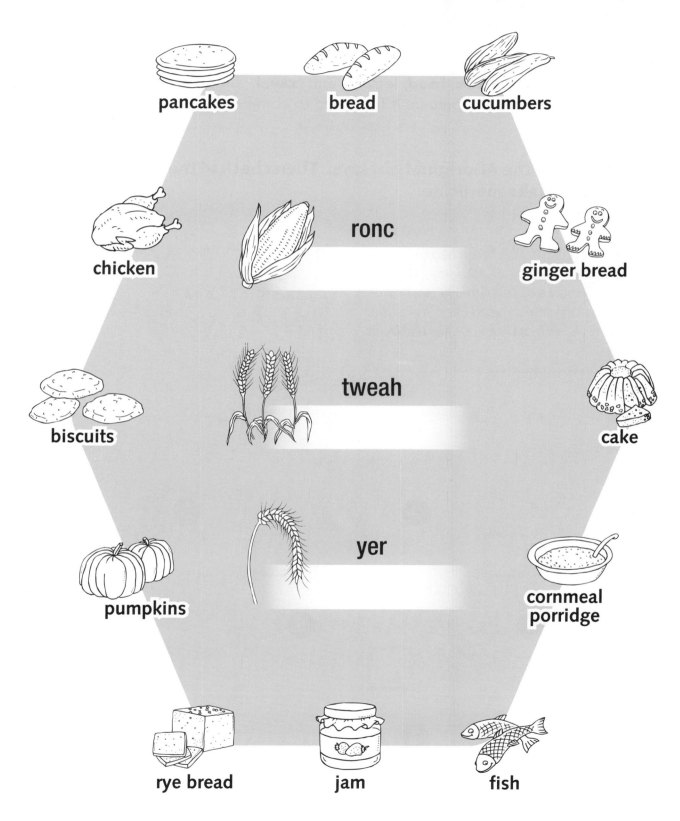

pancakes

bread

cucumbers

chicken

ronc

ginger bread

biscuits

tweah

cake

pumpkins

yer

cornmeal porridge

rye bread

jam

fish

ISBN: 978-1-897164-31-0

14

Learning from Aboriginal Peoples

The settlers learned many things from Aboriginal peoples, like **medicine**, **food**, **leisure**, and **travel**. They also learned how to grow corn and prepare it from seed to cornmeal.

A. **Read what the Aboriginal girl says. Then check ✔ the things that were used to make medicine.**

> *We can make medicine from different parts of plants, like the bark of a tree, the flowers and roots of certain plants, and even fruit, like berries. We can also make tea from leaves.*

1. ☐

2. ☐

3. ☐

4. ☐

5. ☐

6. ☐

7. ☐

8. ☐

ISBN: 978-1-897164-31-0

B. Draw lines to match the different areas of settler life with the sentences.

• The settlers learned how to grow corn.

• Every part of the witch hazel plant had healing properties.

• Canoes were one of the best ways to travel around Upper Canada.

food •

travel •

• The game of lacrosse was an important part of the Iroquoian culture.

medicine •

leisure •

• Tea made from spruce tree twigs cured scurvy, the sailor's disease.

• The settlers learned how to travel over snow using snowshoes.

• The settlers learned how and where to trap animals.

C. Show how corn goes from seed to cornmeal. Colour to show the path.

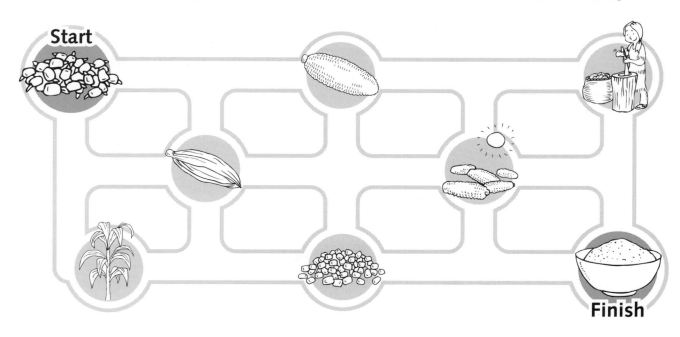

ISBN: 978-1-897164-31-0

15

Maple Syrup

The maple tree was very important. It was the settlers' only source of sugar.

A. Read about maple syrup. Then put each set of pictures in order. Write 1 to 4.

The settlers got their sugar from the sugarbush, a stand of sugar maple trees. The sweet sap started its flow in late winter, long before the leaves appeared. The settlers collected the sap by making a hole in the tree trunk and then poking a wooden tube, called a spile, into it. A bucket placed below the tube caught the sap as it dripped out.

With many buckets filled, the sap was poured into a big pot over a fire. The heat evaporated the water from the sap. As there was less and less water, there was more and more sugar in the liquid. The settlers boiled it down to a thick syrup, which could be used for baking or to sweeten porridge. Some of the syrup was boiled down even more to make taffy – a tasty treat – and finally, maple sugar.

ISBN: 978-1-897164-31-0

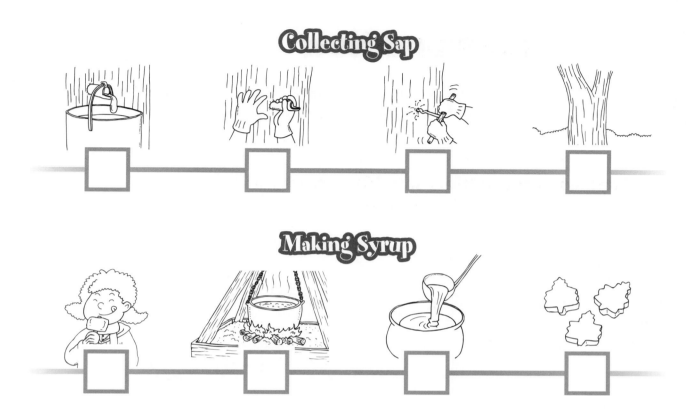

Collecting Sap

Making Syrup

B. **Fill in the missing letters with the help of the given words and pictures.**

sugarbush	syrup	sugar	sweet
spile	snow	sap	

1. __ __p

2. __ug__ __

3. __ __ru__

4. __ __ow

5. __ __e__ __

6. __ __ile

7. __ __ga__b__ __ __

ISBN: 978-1-897164-31-0

16

Then and Now

Many things about life in Canada have changed since the days of the settlers. But some things have stayed the same.

A. **Read what the settlers say. Then cross out ✗ the tools that they do not have.**

> *Our tools are made of wood or metal. Our farm tools are all powered by hand. Fire is our fuel and source of light.*

1. Kitchen Tools

 A
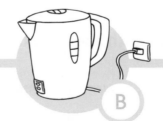 B
 C

2. Farm Tools

 A
 B
 C

3. Lighting

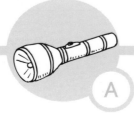 A
 B
 C

ISBN: 978-1-897164-31-0

B. Read what Peter says. Then circle "T" for the true sentences and "F" for the false ones.

> *When my great great grandpa was a kid, he played hoop and stick, checkers, hopscotch, I Spy, and games with marbles. He also went sledding. My friends and I still play the same things, except for hoop and stick. We play computer games.*

1. Hoop and stick is played by both the settler children and today's children.   T   F

2. Computer games are played by today's children only.   T   F

3. Sledding is an activity enjoyed by both the settler children and today's children.   T   F

C. Find out what you share with the settlers' lifestyle. Circle the things that are part of your personal experience.

Food

maple syrup	rabbit
cow's milk	berries
beef stew	squash
ice cream	corn

Way of Travel

wagon	snowshoes
horse	toboggan
sleigh	canoe
ship	foot

ISBN: 978-1-897164-31-0

17

The Compass Rose and the Scale

On a map, the compass rose shows us **directions** while the scale lets us measure the **distances** between places.

A. Write "northeast", "southeast", "southwest", or "northwest".

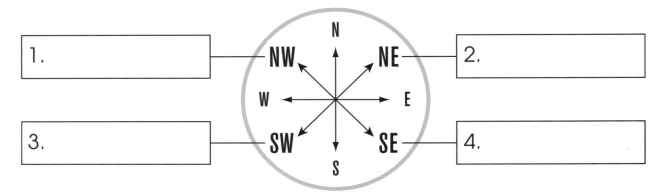

1. _____

2. _____

3. _____

4. _____

B. Look at this picture and fill in the blanks.

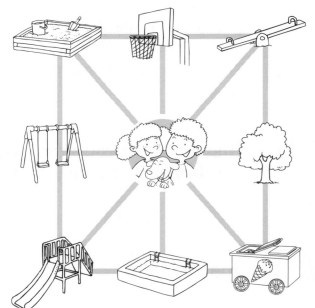

1. Sam wants to play basketball. He should go _____ .

2. Eva wants to play on the swings. She should go _____ . If she wants to play on the slide afterwards, she should go _____ .

3. Benjamin the Dog wants to play in the sand. He should run _____ .

4. They are all playing in the sandbox. If they want some ice cream, they should go _____ .

ISBN: 978-1-897164-31-0

C. **Finish the compass rose with the given directions. Then use the scales on the maps to measure the distances and finish the sentences.**

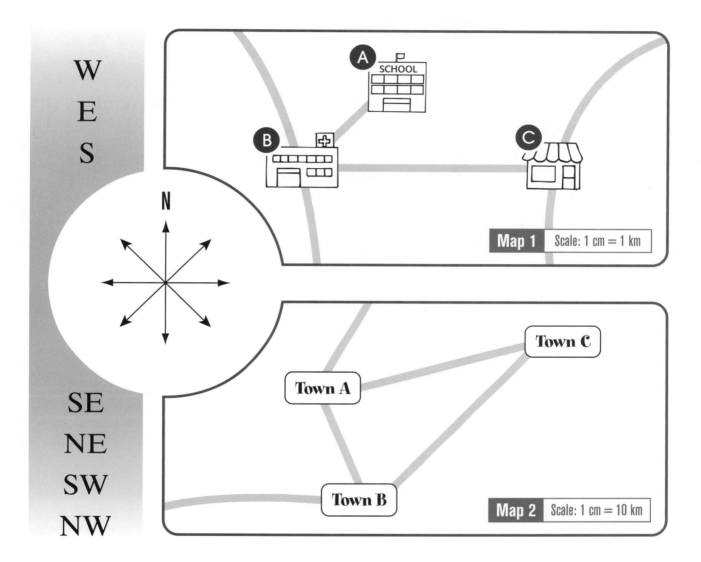

1. Find the distances.

   Map 1   B to C: _____   Map 2   B to C: _____

2. To get from B to A in map 1, you need to go _____ .
   To get from C to B in map 2, you need to go _____ .

3. Map 2 needs a bigger scale than map 1 because _____

   _____ .

ISBN: 978-1-897164-31-0

18

The Legend

The legend has **symbols** to tell us what is on a map. We can also use it to learn more about Canada.

A. Finish the compass rose with the given directions. Then follow the instructions to finish the map and its legend.

S   E   W   SE   NW

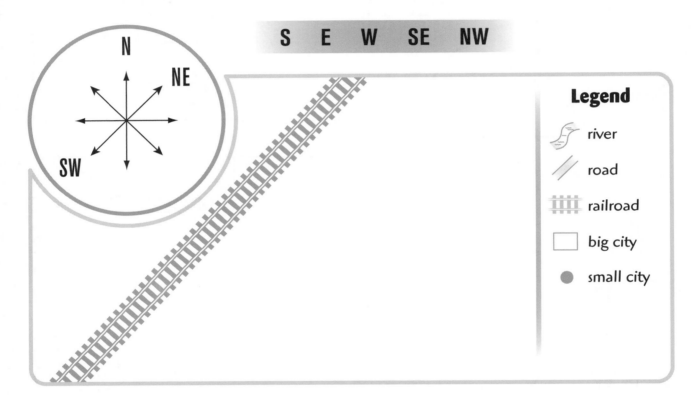

Legend

river

road

railroad

big city

small city

1. Draw a big city in the centre of the map.

2. Draw a small city southwest of the big city.

3. Connect the two cities with a road.

4. To the east of the cities, draw a river that runs from north to south.

5. *Add a new item to the legend, like a lake or a forest, and draw it on the map.*

ISBN: 978-1-897164-31-0

B. Read the explanations and look at the map to finish the legend. Then do what Simon the Dog says and circle the correct numbers.

- The thick lines are the borders of the provinces and territories.
- Ottawa is the capital city of Canada.
- The Trans Canada Highway runs across the country.
- The highest point of Canada is in the west.

Use red to colour the star in the legend and the stars on the map. There are 10 / 11 / 13 province or territory capital cities, but only 1 / 2 / 3 country capital in Canada.

Legend

lake

province or territory border

province or territory capital ☆

country capital

Trans Canada Highway

highest point

Ottawa

ISBN: 978-1-897164-31-0

More about Maps

Besides having a legend, a compass rose, and a scale, most maps also have a title. Maps also come in different types. Each type is useful for different things.

A. Look at the map. Then circle the correct answers.

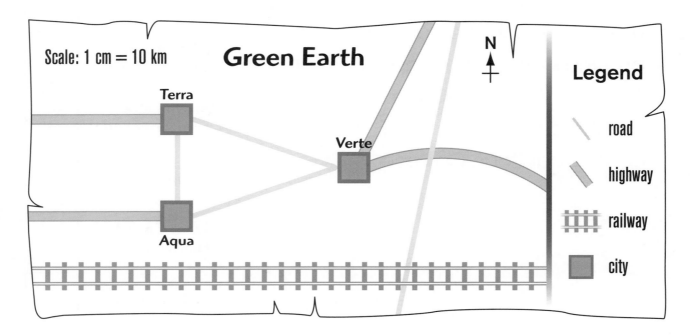

1. There are 30 km / 40 km between Terra and Verte.

2. There are three cities / highways on the map.

3. Aqua is north / south of Terra.

4. The title of the map is _____ .

5. There's a _____ running from east to _____ .

ISBN: 978-1-897164-31-0

B. **Look at these maps. Fill in the blanks with the given words to tell what each map is good for.**

roads   landforms   neighbourhood   location
territories   province   house   lake

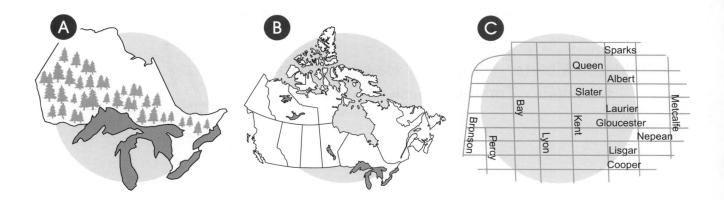

1. Map **A** shows the _____ of a _____ . It is useful when you are looking for a forest or a _____ .

2. Map **B** shows the provinces and _____ of Canada. It is useful when you need to find the _____ of Quebec.

3. Map **C** shows the _____ of a _____ . It is useful when you need to find a friend's _____ .

ISBN: 978-1-897164-31-0

20

A Look at Canada

We can use a compass rose to tell the locations of Canada's **provinces** and **territories**. Also, every province and territory has its own shape, so it is easy to identify.

A. **Look at the map of Canada and label the missing provinces or territories. Then fill in the blanks.**

Yukon   Alberta   Quebec   New Brunswick
Nunavut   Ontario   Saskatchewan

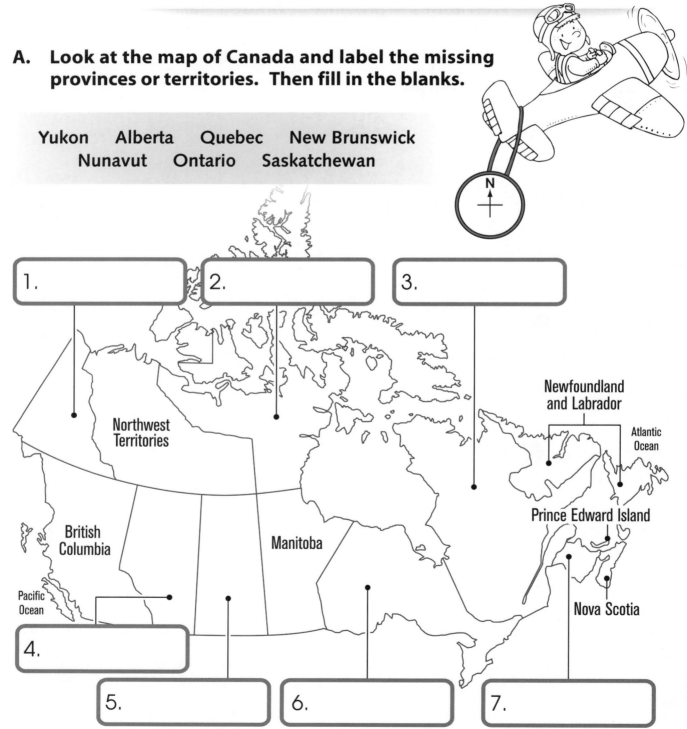

1.

2.

3.

Newfoundland and Labrador

Atlantic Ocean

Northwest Territories

Prince Edward Island

British Columbia

Manitoba

Pacific Ocean

Nova Scotia

4.

5.

6.

7.

ISBN: 978-1-897164-31-0

8. If you are in Ontario, _____ is to the northeast.

9. You are in Nunavut, so _____ is to the south.

10. If you are in Newfoundland and Labrador, the Atlantic Ocean is to the _____ .

11. You are in British Columbia, so the _____ is to the west.

12. If you are in Alberta, you need to go _____ to get to the Northwest Territories.

Pacific Ocean
Manitoba
Quebec
north
east

B. Look again at the map of Canada. Then label these provinces or territories.

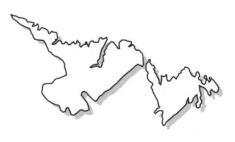

1. _____   2. _____

3. _____   4. _____   5. _____

ISBN: 978-1-897164-31-0

21

A Closer Look at Canada

Every province and territory in Canada has a **capital city** and a **flower symbol**.

A. **Write the capital cities of the provinces and territories.**

Whitehorse   Regina   Edmonton   Toronto   Winnipeg
Iqaluit   Halifax   Fredericton   Victoria   Yellowknife
Charlottetown   St. John's   Québec City

1. Newfoundland and Labrador ★ S_____
2. Prince Edward Island ★ C_____
3. Northwest Territories ★ Y_____
4. British Columbia ★ V_____
5. New Brunswick ★ F_____
6. Nunavut ★ I_____
7. Alberta ★ E_____
8. Yukon ★ W_____
9. Ontario ★ T_____
10. Quebec ★ Q_____
11. Manitoba ★ W_____
12. Nova Scotia ★ H_____
13. Saskatchewan ★ R_____

ISBN: 978-1-897164-31-0

B. **Look at each flower. Fill in the missing letters to complete the name of the province or territory.**

1. fireweed

__ukon

2. wild rose

__lberta

3. trillium

__ntario

4. prairie crocus

__anitoba

5. western red lily

__askatchewan

6. purple saxifrage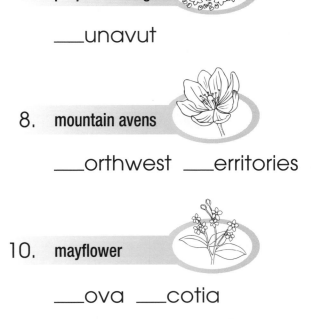

__unavut

7. blue flag iris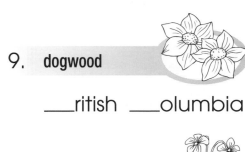

__uebec

8. mountain avens

__orthwest __erritories

9. dogwood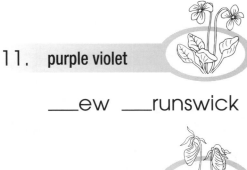

__ritish __olumbia

10. mayflower

__ova __cotia

11. purple violet

__ew __runswick

12. pitcher plant

__ewfoundland and

__abrador

13. lady's slipper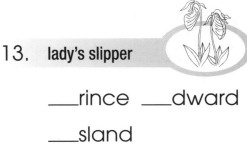

__rince __dward

__sland

ISBN: 978-1-897164-31-0

22

Urban and Rural Communities

Different types of community have different things. An urban community has a **city** environment. A rural community has **country** surroundings. The signs in these communities are different too.

A. See if these belong to an urban, a rural, or both types of community. Write the correct letters on the train cars.

ISBN: 978-1-897164-31-0

B. **Look at the signs. Write "R" for rural or "U" for urban.**

1. Coming Soon –
44-Storey Office Highrise ◯

2. Beaverlodge Trail Rides ◯

3. CAMPFIRE WOOD
SOLD HERE ◯

4. HAY
FOR SALE ◯

5. *Welcome to*
Sunnybrook
Population 200 ◯

6. Population
3 200 000 ◯

7. Elk Crossing
2 km ◯

8. SUBWAY ◯

ISBN: 978-1-897164-31-0

23

Work and Play in Communities

Urban centres and rural places are two different types of environment, so they offer different types of work and play.

A. In which type of community do these things go? Write the correct letters on the buses.

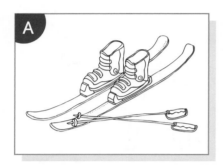

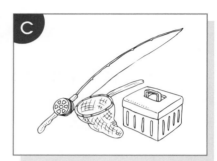

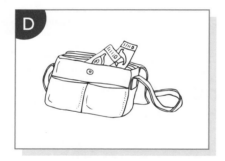

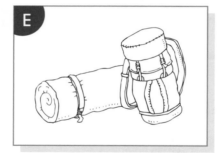

1. Urban

2. Rural

ISBN: 978-1-897164-31-0

B. **Read what these people say. Write the correct letters to tell what summer jobs they have. Then write "urban" or "rural".**

A. stable hand
B. fast food cashier
C. camp leader
D. bike courier

1. *The kids had a lot of fun today. We hiked along a ravine and saw a black bear down below. We also saw salmon in the river and eagles flying overhead. What a fun day!*

_____ _____

2. *There are so many stores in the mall. I work at Healthy Wraps in the food court. I've made lots of friends already!*

_____ _____

3. *Ever since I started working here, I've learned a lot about horses. When I finish my chores each day, I get to take a horse with me for a ride.*

_____ _____

4. *This is a crazy job. There's so much traffic around me, but I'm happy to be using my bike to deliver things. I'm always on the go!*

_____ _____

ISBN: 978-1-897164-31-0

24

Urban and Rural Transportation

People in urban centres have different transportation needs than those in rural areas, but some types of transportation can be found in both types of community.

A. **Label these types of transportation with the given words. Then write the correct letters.**

subway   horse   tractor   streetcar

wagon   taxi   double-decker   logging truck

1.
A

B

C

D

E _____

F _____

G

H _____

2. **Urban** : _____

   Rural : _____

ISBN: 978-1-897164-31-0

B. **Show how these types of transportation can be found in both urban and rural communities. Draw them in each of these pictures.**

bus

train

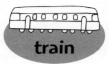
boat

ferry

car

truck

Urban Community

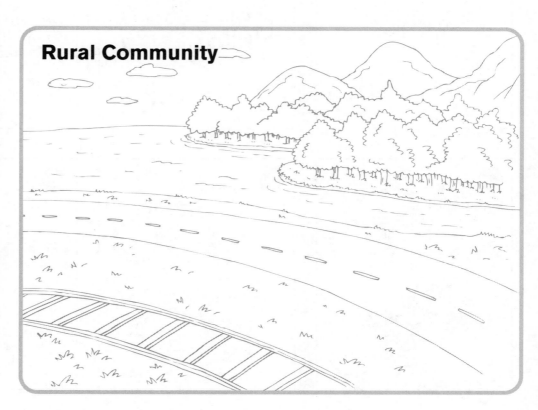
Rural Community

ISBN: 978-1-897164-31-0

Review

A. You are watching a slide show in class. Match the pictures with the given words. Write the correct letters.

A. Three Sisters   B. wigwam

C. fishing hook   D. canoe

E. snowshoes   F. spear

G. moccasins   H. bark

I. longhouse

1

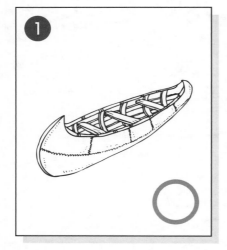

2

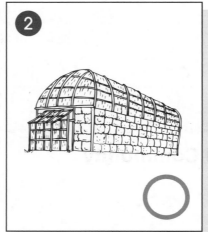

3

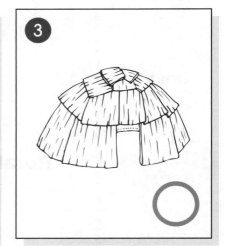

4

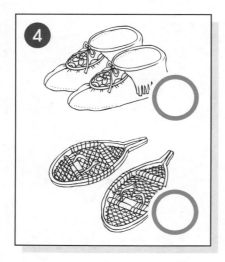

5

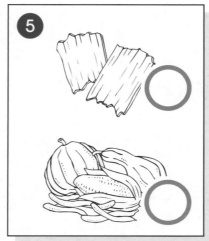

6

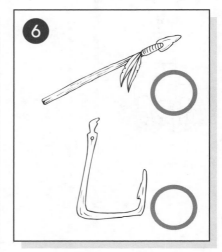

ISBN: 978-1-897164-31-0

B. **Look at the Aboriginal children. See what they are wearing and holding. Then circle the correct words to complete the descriptions.**

1

necklace of corn husks / kernels

dress / breechcloth

basket made of bark / corn

mat made of corn husks / cobs

2

moose call made of bark / corn

canoe / toboggan

moccasins with bark / fur

3

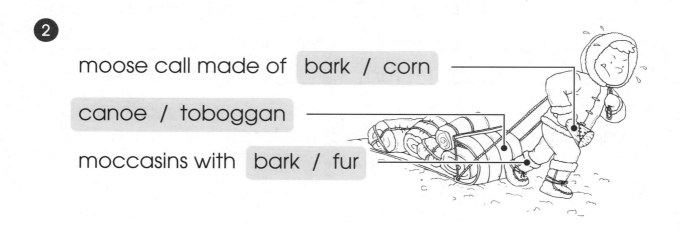

mask of corn husks / kernels

leaves for making sap / tea

pants / leggings

C. **You are looking at a slide of a settler community. Fill in the blanks with the given words to complete what the teacher says. Then circle the correct pictures.**

land   Scotland   States
Germany   jobs   food

1. People came from many different places, like Britain,

   _____ , Ireland, _____ , and even the United

   _____ . They came to Canada for new _____

   to grow _____ , for _____ , and for freedom.

2. What the settlers used to clear the land:

3. The settlers' source of cheese:

4. What the settlers used to build their houses:

ISBN: 978-1-897164-31-0

D. **In art class, your teacher shows you how to make some settler things. Circle the correct answers.**

1. Horseshoes were made by a
    blacksmith / miller .

2. The settlers learned to make
    medicine from the seeds / roots
    of certain plants.

3. Some things that the settlers grew for
    food were potatoes / blueberries and
    wheat / raspberries .

4. The settlers collected sap from birch / maple trees to
    make syrup.

5. Some things the settlers made from meal or flour were
    bread / jam and stew / porridge .

6. The settlers used the grist mill / blacksmith to grind wheat,
    rye, and nuts / corn .

7. The sawyer / wagon maker was someone who made
    wheels.

ISBN: 978-1-897164-31-0

E. You are dressed up as an Aboriginal child from 1800 in a role play. Your classmates are introducing today's Canada to you. Look at the provinces and territories and fill in the missing information.

Flower Symbol

purple saxifrage   fireweed
trillium   blue flag iris

1

Name: _____

Capital: T_____

Flower: t_____

2

Name: _____

Capital: Q_____

Flower: b_____

3

Name: _____

Capital: W_____

Flower: f_____

4

Name: _____

Capital: I_____

Flower: p_____

ISBN: 978-1-897164-31-0

F. **Later in the role play, your classmates show you a map. Fill in the blanks with the correct directions and circle the correct words.**

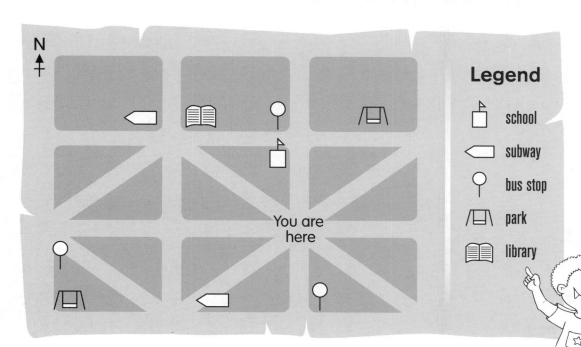

Legend

- school
- subway
- bus stop
- park
- library

You are here

N

1. If you want to take the subway, you need to

   go _____ or _____ .

2. If you want to play at the nearest park, you need to go

   _____ . If you want to go to the library afterwards,

   you need to go _____ .

3. If you want to take the bus after going to the library, you

   need to go _____ .

4. The map above is a   physical / road   map

   showing   an urban / a rural   community.

ISBN: 978-1-897164-31-0

ISBN: 978-1-897164-31-0

1 Plants

- Different parts of a plant work together to make a healthy plant.
- Different kinds of plants have parts that do the same job, but they may not look alike.
- A tree can be described as broadleaf or coniferous.

A. **Write the correct part of a plant on the line.**

stem   flower   roots   leaves

This is the 1._____
It is sweet, not sour
Making seeds for new plants
Is the flower's power

These are the 2._____
The greens that breathe
Food for the plant
Is what they achieve

This is the 3._____
That's holding them
Food up and food down
From end to end

These are the 4._____
Like spongy boots
They take water and food
To send up to the shoots

B. **Label the parts of the plant.**

stem
leaf
root
flower

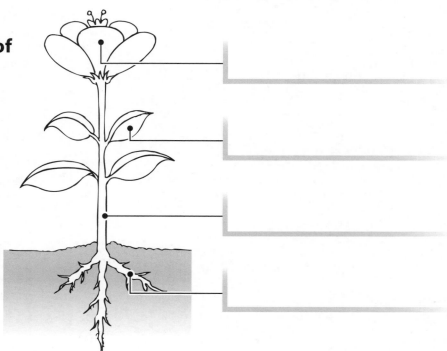

ISBN: 978-1-897164-31-0

C. Unscramble the words to name the parts of a tree. Then draw lines to match the names with the parts.

1. arbk   b_____ •

2. nuktr   t_____ •

3. veales   l_____ •

4. troos   r_____ •

5. abrchnse   b_____ •

D. Match each description with the correct type of tree. Write the letter.

Broadleaf Tree

○○○

Coniferous Tree

○○○

A most have leaves that change colour in the fall

B often have needle-shaped leaves

C deciduous trees belong to this group

D most are evergreen

E seeds found in cones

F have wide, flat leaves

Science Fact

Trees are the largest kind of plant. While some trees will never be as tall as you, there are others that are taller than a 15-storey building!

ISBN: 978-1-897164-31-0

Leaves and Flowers

- *Although leaves have different shapes and sizes, they do the same job.*
- *Each part of a flower has a different job to do.*

A. **Draw the other half of each leaf. Then match the leaf with the name of the plant. Write the letter.**

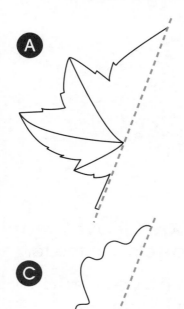

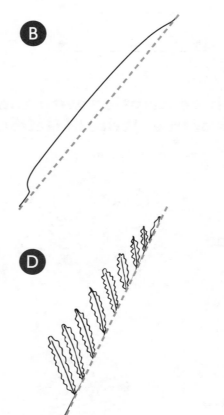

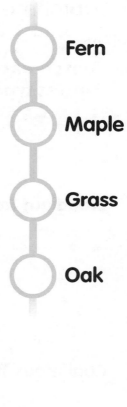

Fern

Maple

Grass

Oak

B. **Match the descriptions with the plants above. Write the names of the plants on the lines.**

1. These long and narrow leaves grow outward all season. _____

2. The leaves of this plant unfold from a coiled position when they first appear. _____

ISBN: 978-1-897164-31-0

C. Use the flower clues and the given words to complete the names of the parts of the flower. Then answer the questions.

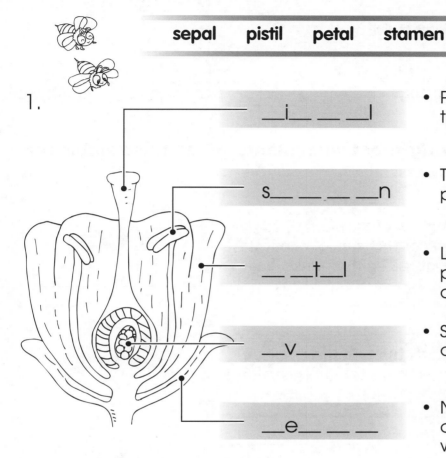

sepal pistil petal stamen ovary

1.

__ i__ __ __l

- Pollen reaches the ovary through this stalk.

s__ __.__ __n

- This is the pollen-producing part.

__ __t__l

- Like a colourful leaf, this protects the flower and attracts pollinators.

__v__ __ __

- Seeds form here if pollination occurs.

__e__ __ __

- Now at the flower's base, it covered the flower when it was just a bud.

2.

Which part of the flower is at the base of the pistil and is a place for seed development?

_____

3.

Which part of the flower is usually green and protects the bud?

_____

Science Fact

Some plants have special leaves that are not flowers, but look like them. The true flowers of the dogwood tree and poinsettia are barely noticeable inside the colourful imposters.

poinsettia

ISBN: 978-1-897164-31-0

The Needs of Plants

- Plants need air, light, and water to live and be healthy.
- Plants have adapted ways of getting what they need from their environment.

A. The children are talking about what plants need. Unscramble the letters to find the answers.

1.

   It goes in and out of the plant through special parts of the leaf. Without it, leaves cannot use light to make food. What is it?

   r i a

   _____

2.

   It enters plants through their roots in the ground. It helps take nutrients to all parts of the plant. What is it?

   a w t r e

   _____

3.

   It comes from the sun. Leaves use it to make food. What is it?

   t g h l i

   _____

Experiment

Completely cover a plant leaf by folding a piece of black construction paper over it. Attach a piece of tape to keep it closed. After a few days look underneath the paper.

What does the leaf look like? Of the three things a plant needs, what could not reach that part of the leaf?

ISBN: 978-1-897164-31-0

B. Write the correct words to complete the sentences. Then show where each plant belongs. Write the letter.

1.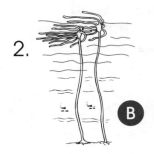

   Cacti have thin ＿＿＿＿＿＿＿ that retain water,
   leaves / flowers
   and ＿＿＿＿＿＿＿ stems that store water.
   thin / thick
   Because of this, they do not need a regular
   source of water.

2.

   Bull kelp has an air-filled bulb that will
   ＿＿＿＿＿＿＿ on the ocean's surface. This is
   float / walk
   how the leaves get ＿＿＿＿＿＿＿ .
   water / sunlight

3.

   These plants grow in clumps close to the
   ＿＿＿＿＿＿＿ . They protect themselves from
   ground / tree
   cold and wind this way.

4.

   The trillium grows, flowers, and dies within the first
   few weeks of spring before emerging tree
   ＿＿＿＿＿＿＿ completely shade the forest floor.
   roots / leaves

alpine	desert	water	woodland
◯	◯	◯	◯

 **Science Fact**

Plants can "move". The leaves of a houseplant move to face a window, and sunflowers follow the daily movement of the sun.

ISBN: 978-1-897164-31-0

Plants: Pollination

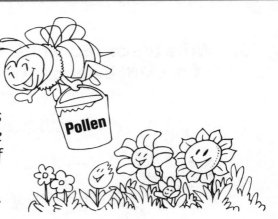

- When the pollen from one plant's stamen reaches the pistil of another, pollination occurs. The pollinated plant can now produce seeds capable of growing into new plants.
- Animals and wind are the pollinators of some plants.

A. Find the most likely pollinator for each plant. Write the answer on the line.

| hummingbird | wind |
| moth | bee | butterfly |

1. Because this pollinator works in the evening, easily seen white flowers are a favourite.

   _____

   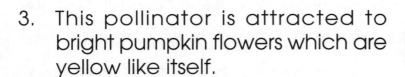

2. This pollinator likes to land on the bright flower clusters of this plant.

   _____

3. This pollinator is attracted to bright pumpkin flowers which are yellow like itself.

   _____

4. The silk of the corn plant is slightly sticky at pollination time. It makes it easier to "catch" the pollen.

   _____

5. The fuchsia's pollinator must reach the nectar through the long, narrow blossom.

   _____

   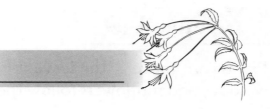 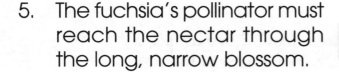

ISBN: 978-1-897164-31-0

B. **Fill in the blanks with the given words. Then find the examples of flowers for each kind of pollination.**

animals   wind
small   colours

Animal pollination:

* The flowers pollinated by _____ always have bright _____ , strong scents, and sweet nectar.

* Examples: _____

Wind pollination:

* The flowers pollinated by_____ are always _____ and not colourful.

* Examples: _____

C. **Find the correct word to match each description.**

stamen   pistil   pollen   scent   nectar   seed

1. _____ – tiny grains made by the stamen
2. _____ – the part of the flower that makes pollen
3. _____ – the part of the flower that receives pollen
4. _____ – what develops when pollination occurs
5. _____ – what animals smell that attracts them to flowers
6. _____ – a rewarding drink for pollinating animals

Science Fact

Pollination is not just good for the flowers. Honey is made from the nectar collected by honeybees while they pollinate.

ISBN: 978-1-897164-31-0

Seed Dispersion

Seed dispersion.

- *Seeds spread themselves around so they do not all grow in the same area. This is called seed dispersion.*
- *Plants have developed different ways of dispersing their seeds.*

A. Match the seed with the method of dispersal. Write the letter.

A Like parachutes, they are carried by a breeze.

B Eaten by animals, they are eventually deposited far away.

C The seeds are forcefully expelled from the pod.

D Floating to its new home, it is carried away by ocean currents.

E It hitches a ride with a furry animal, or a fuzzy shoe.

F With its helicopter wings, it spins to the ground.

G Rolling like a wheel, its seeds travel far.

ISBN: 978-1-897164-31-0

B. **Put the sentences in the correct order to show how the seeds are dispersed. Write 1 to 3. Then tell what method each plant uses to disperse its seeds.**

1

◯ A ripe berry drops onto the water, floating to its new home.

◯ Water levels rise around a maturing cranberry bush.

◯ The water recedes, the berry seed germinates, and a new cranberry bush sprouts.

by _____

2

◯ Fluffy hairs on the seeds allow even a small breeze to carry them away.

◯ Fireweed seedlings grow far from the parent plant.

◯ Pods of the fireweed split open to release tiny seeds.

by _____

3

◯ Acorns fall from oak trees in fall.

◯ A new oak tree sprouts in spring.

◯ A squirrel packs a few in its cheeks, but drops one or two along the way.

by _____

Science Fact

Very large seeds often depend on gravity for dispersal. They can gain distance from the parent plant by rolling down slopes and mountainsides.

ISBN: 978-1-897164-31-0

6

Plants: Life Cycles

- Different plants have similar cycles of growth and reproduction.
- While some plants can live for hundreds of years, others complete their life cycle within a year.

A. Draw pictures to complete the life cycle of a pumpkin with the help of the pictures on the left.

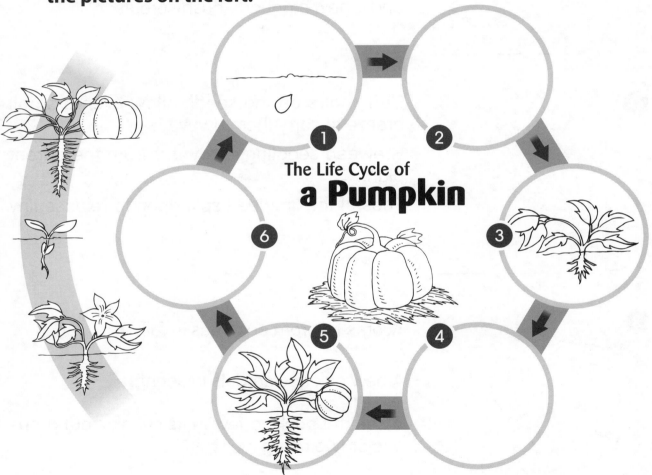

The Life Cycle of
a Pumpkin

B. Put the life cycle of a flower in the correct order. Write the letters.

Life Cycle of a Flower

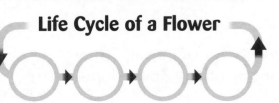

ISBN: 978-1-897164-31-0

C. **Fill in the blanks with the correct words to complete the life cycle comparison.**

Life Cycles of  and

months	years
maple tree	leaves
flowers	sunflower

1. It takes many _____ for a maple tree to grow to maturity and produce seeds. A sunflower completes its life cycle within a few _____ .

2. The maple tree and sunflower grow many _____ before their _____ and seeds form.

3. The maple tree and sunflower both start as small seeds, but the _____ grows to be much larger than the _____ .

D. **Draw lines to give examples of these kinds of plants.**

Annual plants •

Biennial plants •

Perennial plants •

• A pumpkin plant sprouts and dies within one year.

• Many plants, including all trees, can live for many years.

• Parsley and foxgloves are examples of plants that live for two years.

 **Science Fact**

Olive trees grow slowly, but can live a very long life. Some don't bear fruit until they reach 30 years or older, but they continue to produce olives for hundreds of years.

ISBN: 978-1-897164-31-0

7

Uses of Plants

- We use plants for many different things, from medicine to furniture and clothing.
- How we use particular plants or their parts depends on their characteristics.

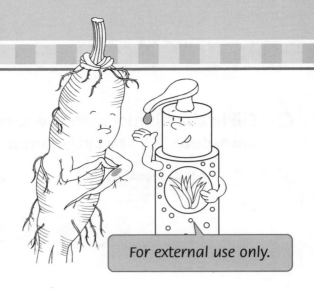

For external use only.

A. **Circle the words that describe the characteristics of the plants. Then match the plants with the things that can be made with them.**

1. The hard wood of the oak tree makes sturdy floors. _____

2. Rope is made from the strong fibres of the sisal plant. _____

3. Sweet juice from the sugar cane gives us sugar for tea and for baking. _____

4. The soft, light wood of the pine tree is ideal as a building material. _____

5. The stem of the rattan palm is flexible and strong, making it ideal for making furniture. _____

6. The soft, fine hairs of the cotton plants are made into fabric for clothing. _____

7. The flexible substance that oozes from the rubber tree makes rubber for bike tires. _____

ISBN: 978-1-897164-31-0

B. **Fill in the missing letters to match each part of the pine tree with the product that it makes.**

needles   bark   trunk   sap

1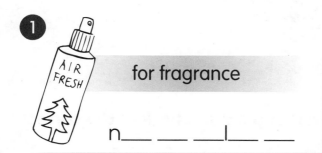

for fragrance

n__ __ __l__ __

2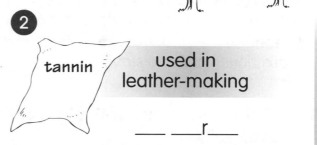

tannin

used in leather-making

__ __r__

3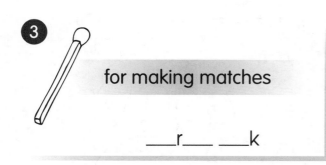

for making matches

__r__ __k

4

for cleaning paint from brushes

__ __p

C. **Read what Lucy says. Then unscramble the word to see what the things are made from.**

Coffee   Sunflower oil   Peanut Butter   Mustard

Although these products are all made from different plants, they are made from the same part of a plant. What is it?

e s d e

the _____

Science Fact

Plants are more than useful to us; all other living things, including humans, cannot live without them. They give us oxygen to breathe, and are the base of all our food sources.

ISBN: 978-1-897164-31-0

8

Endangered Plants or Invasive Plants

- When new plants take over a land, they may become invasive plants because they make native plants struggle for survival.
- Endangered plants are those that need protection in order to survive.

A. Find the reasons for the loss of habitat of plants. Check ✔ the correct letters.

- (A) vehicles driving off-road
- (B) fertilizing fields
- (C) over-picking flowers
- (D) trampling on plants
- (E) spraying pesticides
- (F) watering plants
- (G) planting saplings in a new field
- (H) clearing land for growing crops
- (I) new species taking over a field
- (J) clearing land for animals to graze
- (K) clearing land for houses, shopping malls, or other buildings

 ISBN: 978-1-897164-31-0

B. **Write "Invasive" or "Endangered" to complete the titles. Then colour the flowers as specified.**

E_____ Plants

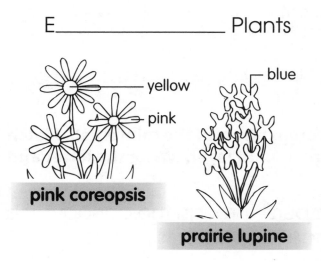

yellow
pink
blue

pink coreopsis

prairie lupine

I_____ Plants

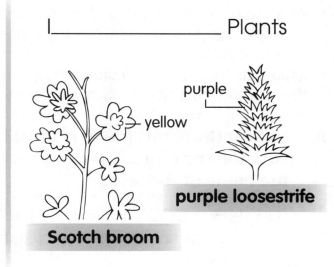

purple
yellow

purple loosestrife

Scotch broom

C. **Fill in the blanks with the given words to complete the paragraph.**

extinct   endangered   invasive
habitat   protected   native

Every time a forest or meadow is cleared for human development, some plants lose their 1._____ . If a plant is rare, or its habitat is special, it may be in danger of becoming 2._____ . There are many 3._____ plants in Canada. Some are 4._____ by laws, and many conservation groups are trying to save them from extinction. They remove the 5._____ plants and grow more 6._____ plants in their place.

Science Fact

Many invasive plants are very beautiful, and sometimes useful to humans. Scotch broom is admired while it is in bloom, and Himalayan blackberries are a sweet treat in late summer.

Himalayan blackberries

9

Rainforests

- *Rainforests are the habitat of many plants and animals. They have heavy rainfall and hot or mild temperatures.*
- *Almost all rainforests are found in regions around the equator. These are tropical rainforests.*

A. Look at the plants found in the different layers of the rainforest. Match each description with the correct plant and layer. Write the letter and the name of the layer.

1. This tree is one of the few that burst through the canopy. It is assured of sunshine, and space to spread its leaves.

   _____ ; _____

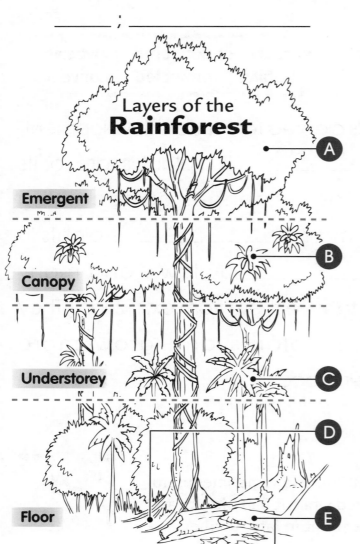

Layers of the **Rainforest**

Emergent

Canopy

Understorey

Floor

2. Tall trees send down buttress roots for extra support.

   _____ ; _____

3. Fallen logs and dead leaves feed the soil that nourishes the forest.

   _____ ; _____

4. An orchid grows on a branch to get its share of sunshine.

   _____ ; _____

5. The palm is a tree that grows in shade, below the forest canopy.

   _____ ; _____

ISBN: 978-1-897164-31-0

B. **Fill in the blanks with the given words to complete the passage.**

canopy   birds   rainfall   seeds   vines   layer   animals
understorey   plants   forest floor   dense   fruits

The Rainforest Canopy

An amazing variety of 1._____ and

2._____ live in rainforests. Most animals

are found in the 3._____ , enjoying the

4._____ and 5._____ , and the sun

when it shines. 6._____ easily fly from treetop to

treetop, but this 7._____ is so 8._____

that even flightless animals have no trouble getting

around. The busy canopy weathers almost daily

9._____ , acting like a leaky umbrella to the

10._____ and 11._____ . It also shades

the plants below, making 12._____ and

smaller trees struggle to reach light.

Science Fact

Canada is home to a temperate rainforest. It stretches
along British Columbia's mild west coast.

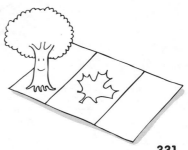

ISBN: 978-1-897164-31-0

10

Force as a Push or Pull

Pull harder!

- A *force* is a push or pull that one thing exerts upon another.
- Forces can be of two types: pushes and pulls of objects that make contact, and those that are at work from a distance.

A.   Identify the force(s) in each picture. Write "Push", "Pull", or "Both Push and Pull" on the line.

1.

_____

2.

_____

3.

_____

4.
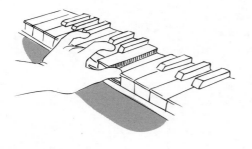
_____

5.

_____

ISBN: 978-1-897164-31-0

B. Fill in the blanks with "g", "t", "v", or "r" to complete the "force" words.

1.

____ra____ity

2.

s____a____ic

elec____ ____ici____y

3.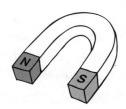

ma____ne____ism

C. Identify the type of force in each picture.

Types of Forces
- **Direct Contact** or **From a Distance**
- **Push** or **Pull**

1. _____ ; _____
2. _____ ; _____
3. _____ ; _____
4. _____ ; _____

Science Fact

When you are standing still on the ground, you are exerting a force downwards on the ground. The ground is exerting a force of the same size upwards on you.

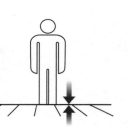

ISBN: 978-1-897164-31-0

11

Forces and Movement

- Forces acting upon objects that are not moving occur in pairs: equal in size but opposite in direction. They are balanced.
- Unbalanced forces that act upon an object will result in movement or a change in movement of that object.

A. Draw an arrow in each picture to balance the force.

1

2

3

4

5

6

ISBN: 978-1-897164-31-0

B. **Put the pictures in order. Write 1 to 3. Then colour the one that shows where the forces become unbalanced.**

1.

2.

3.

🧪 **Science Fact**

Walking is controlled falling. While standing still, you are balanced. When you lift your foot and push with your other foot, you become unbalanced. Balance is returned when you put your foot down again. You have moved forward.

ISBN: 978-1-897164-31-0

Gravity

- Gravity is a pulling force on things.
- The heavier or bigger the object, the greater the force of gravity.

A. Draw an arrow if the picture shows gravity at work; otherwise, write "No Gravity" on the line.

1.

2.

3.

4.

5.

ISBN: 978-1-897164-31-0

B. **Look at the planets. Put them in order from the one with the greatest gravity to the one that has the least. Write their names on the lines. Then answer the questions.**

1.

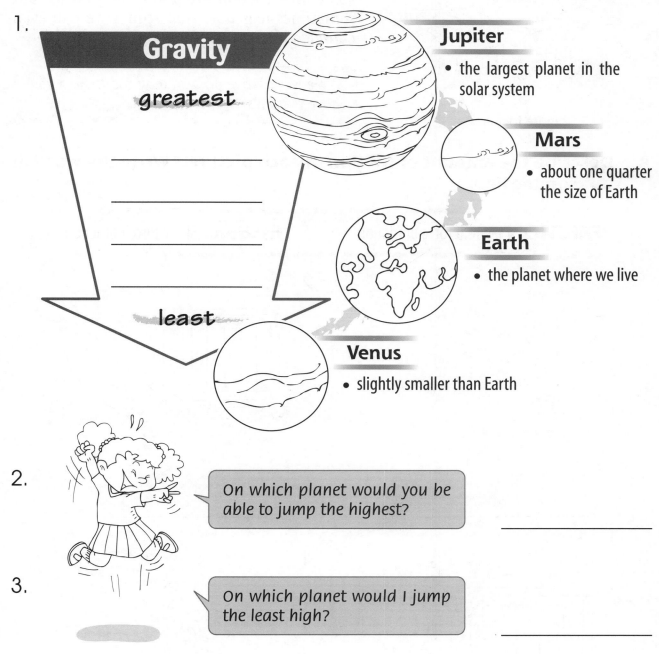

Gravity

greatest

_____

_____

_____

least

Jupiter
- the largest planet in the solar system

Mars
- about one quarter the size of Earth

Earth
- the planet where we live

Venus
- slightly smaller than Earth

2. On which planet would you be able to jump the highest?

_____

3. On which planet would I jump the least high?

_____

Science Fact

In order to function properly, a ballpoint pen needs the force of gravity. In space or on the space station, it would not work.

ISBN: 978-1-897164-31-0

13

Friction

more fricton

- Friction is *a force that happens when two objects rub against each other.* Its direction is opposite the direction of movement.
- Sometimes friction is a good thing for us, but sometimes it is not. Sometimes we can even change the amount of friction.

It's easy to drive on a muddy road when you have tires with *deeper tracks.*

A. Describe the amount of friction in each picture. Write the word in bold on the line.

FRICTION – great force of friction   **friction** – small force of friction

1.

_____

2.

_____

3.

_____

4.

_____

 ISBN: 978-1-897164-31-0

B. **Help the magazine editors answer the letters dealing with friction problems. Fill in the blanks with the given words.**

1

Dear Editors,
I know to use environmentally friendly car wash detergent and a soft cloth to clean my car, but sometimes I can't get all the dirt off. What can I do?

Thanks,
Jim-Bob McGillicutty

Use a _____ sponge to
_{rough/soft}

_____ friction.
_{increase/reduce}

2

Dear Editors,
What can I do to increase the friction that is needed to clean my teeth?

Yours truly,
Sofie Cannie

Use a brush with _____
_{softer/harder}
bristles.

3

Dear Editors,
The chain on my bicycle is old and I think it is making it hard for me to pedal. Any suggestions?

Thanks,
Peter Pedalstire

Use _____ to
_{bicycle grease/water}

_____ friction.
_{increase/reduce}

4

Dear Editors,
We have new shiny wooden floors in our house, but everyone keeps falling down when they are wearing socks. What should we do?

Sincerely,
Rebecca Salks

Wear _____
_{bigger socks/slippers with rubber soles}

to _____ friction.
_{increase/decrease}

Science Fact

It is not because ice is really slippery that you can skate so fast. When you glide over the ice, the heat caused by the skate blade rubbing against the ice causes the ice to melt underneath it. You are actually gliding on water, and that is what reduces the friction and makes sliding so easy.

ISBN: 978-1-897164-31-0

14

Magnets

- A magnet is a piece of iron that has a special force: magnetism.
- Magnetism is a force that can push or pull other objects that are magnetic.

A. Which objects are magnetic? Draw lines from the magnetic objects to the horseshoe magnet.

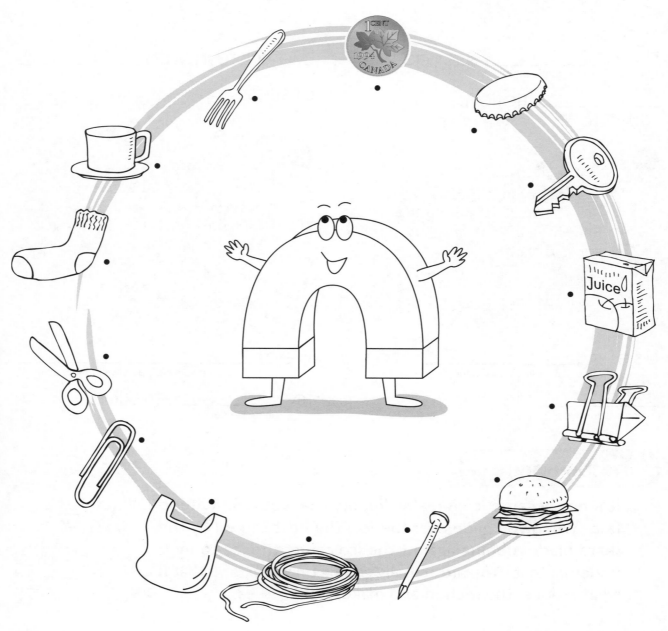

ISBN: 978-1-897164-31-0

B. Read what the mouse says. Unscramble the letters to find out what materials are not magnetic.

Not all metals are magnetic. Iron, or metal that is mostly iron, is always magnetic.

1
_____
lsasg

2
_____
thloc

3
_____
odow

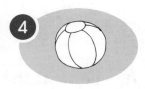

4
_____
sctipla

C. Where are magnets used? Circle the magnets in each picture.

Experiment – Turn a needle into a magnet!

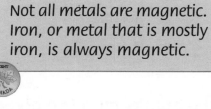

- Stroke the end of the magnet along the length of the needle about 30 times. Stroke in only one direction – do not rub back and forth.
- Test your "magnet". Try to pick up some pins with the needle.

Things needed:
- 1 magnet
- 1 needle

 **Science Fact**

You can pick up dust from outer space with a magnet. Since tiny meteorite particles contain iron, a magnet will pick them up.

ISBN: 978-1-897164-31-0

15

Magnetic Poles

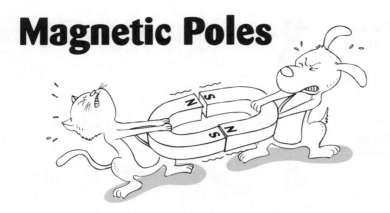

- Every magnet has a south pole and a north pole.
- The Earth behaves like a magnet, with both a south pole and a north pole. Because of this, a magnetic compass shows us which way is north.

A. Look at the pictures. Then fill in the blanks with the given words.

south   north   repels   attracts

1. A magnet has a _____ pole and a _____ pole.

2. The north pole of one magnet _____ the south pole of another magnet.

3. The north pole of one magnet _____ the north pole of another magnet.

B. Write "N" for north pole or "S" for south pole in the circles to complete the diagrams.

Magnets Attract

Magnets Repel

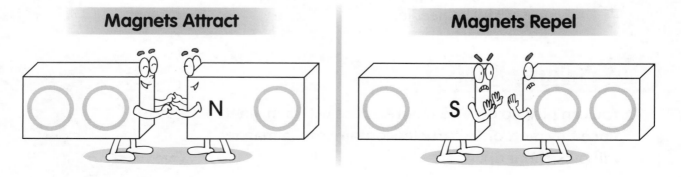

ISBN: 978-1-897164-31-0

C. Fill in the blanks to complete what Dr. Cowan says. Complete each diagram to show how a triangle is formed with three bar magnets.

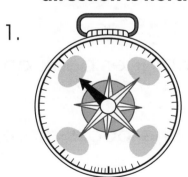

N – north pole
S – south pole

1 A triangle is formed from three bar magnets put together end to end, but they must be put together so the poles

_____ .

attract / repel

 2

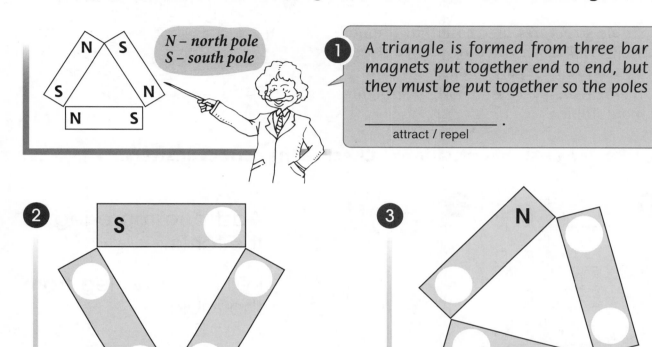

 3

D. For each compass, write "N" in the correct shaded part to show which direction is north.

1.

2.

3.

Science Fact

Repelling magnets are used to give roller coasters a boost at the beginning of the ride. Instead of starting slowly and gradually gaining speed, the fun starts right away!

16

Stability

- Stable structures are those that are not likely to fall down, overturn, or break when reasonable forces are applied to them.
- There are many ways to make a structure more stable.

A. Fix the unstable situations. Check ✔ the correct answers.

1

2

Ⓐ Add one more leg to the table.

Ⓑ Remove one leg from the table.

3

Ⓐ Use training wheels.

Ⓑ Use bigger wheels.

4

Ⓐ Put a bigger book on top.

Ⓑ Stack the books more neatly.

Ⓐ Use a longer ladder.

Ⓑ Pull the "feet" of the ladder farther away from the house.

ISBN: 978-1-897164-31-0

B. **These fairy tale characters have problems with stability. Help them circle the correct words to fix the problems.**

1.

Every time I climb this skinny beanstalk, I think it's going to break and fall down, so I don't get to climb very high.

Solution:

Climb a   thicker / rough   beanstalk.

2.

I've lost two brothers. How can I build my house to keep the wolf out?

Solution:

Build the house out of a   thicker / stronger   material.

3.

Those goats make such a racket on my bridge. I'm afraid they may be too heavy and make it collapse right down onto me!

Solution:

Use   beams / sticks   to support the bridge.

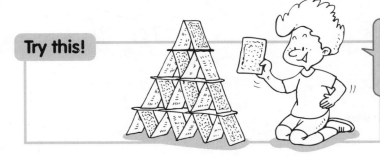

Try this!

Use an ordinary deck of cards to make a house of cards.

Science Fact

Eggshells are not easily crushed when being squeezed because of their arch shape. The arch is a very strong structure that has been used to build bridges for many years.

ISBN: 978-1-897164-31-0

17

Levers

- Levers are simple machines that can make movement and force either larger or smaller.
- The point on which the lever pivots, or turns around, is called the fulcrum.

Open.

A. Colour the tools that are levers.

1.
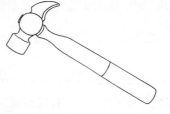

2.

3.

4.
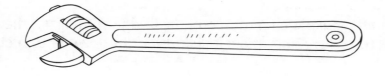

5.

6.
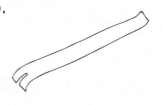

7.

B. Circle the fulcrum in each lever.

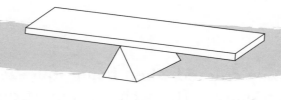

ISBN: 978-1-897164-31-0

C. Read what Daniel says. Help him do the experiment. Then use the given words to complete the record.

You need a broom and an open space to do this experiment. This experiment will tell you what happens when the fulcrum in a lever changes position.

easy   little   easier   harder   greater   lesser

Record

Part 1

Grab the handle of the broom with both hands. Sweep, being careful not to move the fulcrum.

← fulcrum

- _____ to sweep
- broom's sweep length:
  _____

Part 2

Slide your lower hand higher up the handle so that it is closer to your other hand. Sweep, noting any change in the force required to move the broom.

- _____ to sweep
- broom's sweep length:
  _____

Part 3

Slide your lower hand as far down the broom handle as you can. Sweep, again noting any changes in force.

- _____ to sweep
- broom's sweep length:
  _____

Science Fact

The lever is the oldest of the simple machines. A shaduf was used by Egyptians around 3000 BCE. The counterweight made getting the water from the river easier.

ISBN: 978-1-897164-31-0

18

More about Levers

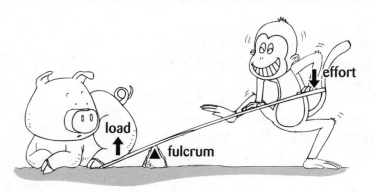

- A lever has three parts: the fulcrum, or pivot point, an effort, or a force that is put into the lever, and the load, which is the force that comes out of the machine.

- Changing the order of the fulcrum, effort force, and load force results in different machines that do different things.

A. Label each lever with "fulcrum", "effort", and "load".

1

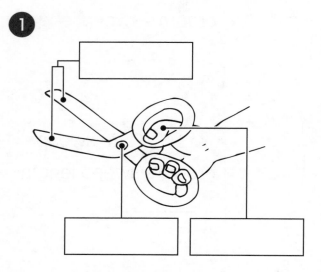

2

3

4

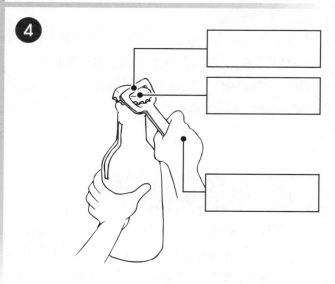

ISBN: 978-1-897164-31-0

B. Look at the pictures. Circle the correct words to complete what Tom says.

1.

A shovel is an example of a

_____ (lever / screw).

2.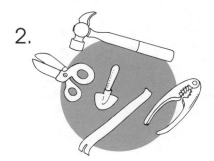

Levers are simple machines that make

work _____ (harder / easier) for us.

3.

The farther the effort force is from the

fulcrum, the _____ (harder / easier)

it is to move the load.

4.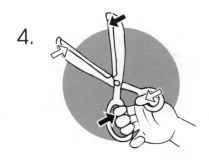

When we use scissors, the small movement

our fingers make will result in a _____

(greater / smaller) movement made by the

blades.

Science Fact

They all make use of
LEVERS.

What do pianos, self-filling fountain pens, and old water pumps
have in common?

ISBN: 978-1-897164-31-0

19

Soil

Hi, Mr. Soil.

- Soil is the top layer of much of the Earth's land surface.
- Soil is a mixture of broken rock, humus (bits of dead plants and animal wastes), air, and water.

A. Colour the soil in the picture brown.

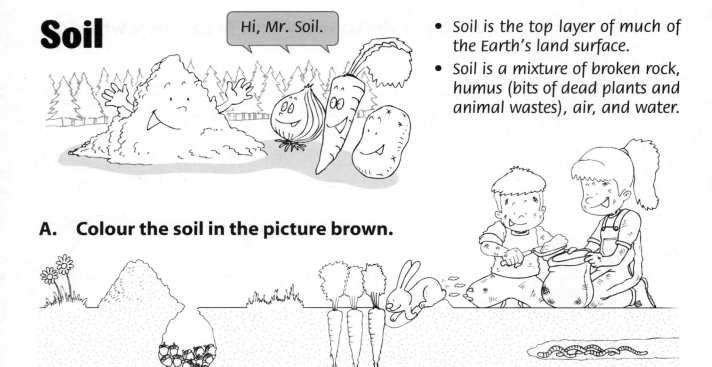

B. See how rock is broken down in nature in each picture. Write the missing letters to find out the natural source.

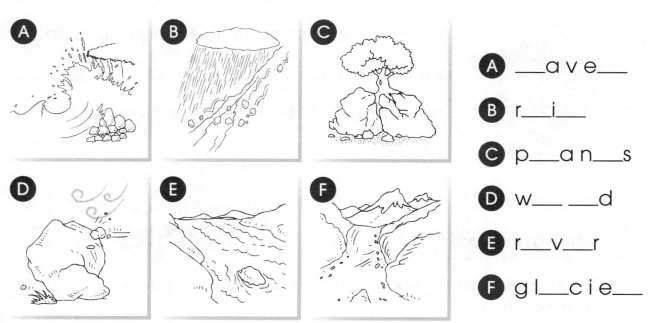

A __ a v e __

B r __ i __

C p __ a n __ s

D w __ __ d

E r __ v __ r

F g l __ c i e __

ISBN: 978-1-897164-31-0

C. **Humus is made from lots of things. Identify the things. Write the letters.**

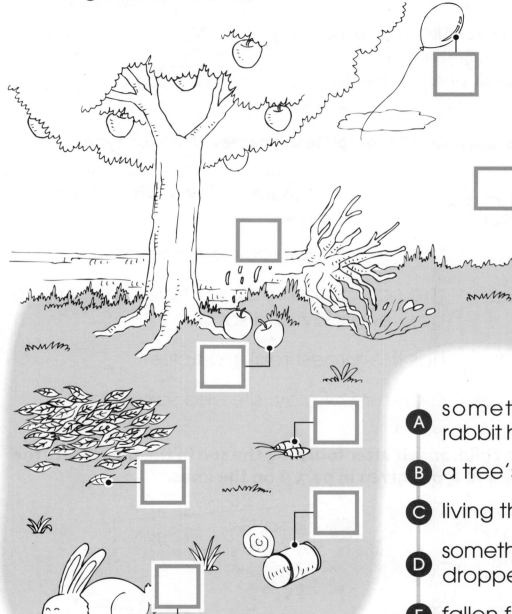

A something that a rabbit has left behind

B a tree's fall offering

C living things

D something a bird has dropped

E fallen fruit

F what's left of a tree

Science Fact

Because rock erosion happens very slowly, it takes thousands of years to make one centimetre of soil.

20

More about Soil

- We classify soil by the size of its rock particles.
- Each type of soil has different textures.
- The different types of soil can be found in different places.

A.   Fill in the missing letters to complete the names of the soil types.

loam   clay   silt   sand

Types of Soil

- __ l __ __: has the smallest rock particles

- __ __ l __: the size of the rock particles that are in between clay and sand

- s__ __d: has the largest rock particles

- __ o __ __: a mixture of clay, silt, and sandy soil

B.   See what the children felt after touching the soil in the box. Write the names of the soil types given in part A on the lines.

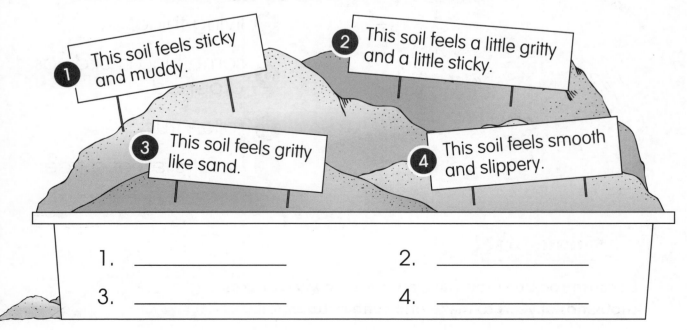

1. This soil feels sticky and muddy.

2. This soil feels a little gritty and a little sticky.

3. This soil feels gritty like sand.

4. This soil feels smooth and slippery.

1. _____   2. _____

3. _____   4. _____

    ISBN: 978-1-897164-31-0

C. **See what types of soil the children and the pig are describing. Write the names of the soil types on the lines.**

clay   silt   sand   loam

1. The rock particles are so small in this soil, there is not a lot of room for air.

   _____

2. This soil holds just enough air and water to keep most plants happy.

   _____

3. With plenty of humus, this soil is used by plant nurseries.

   _____

4.
   a. Water drains easily from this soil.

   _____

   b. This soil absorbs water well.

   _____

   c. When this soil dries, it repels water.

   _____

   d. This soil is sometimes found near beaches.

   _____

Science Fact

We know air and water are ingredients of soil, but they are not just small ingredients. Air and water make up about half of most types of soil.

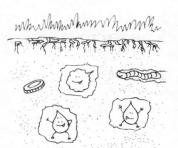

21

Soil Erosion

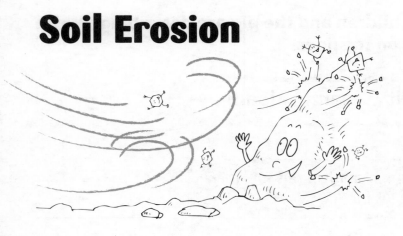

- Soil is lost when it is blown by wind or carried away by rain or rivers. Mountain soil will gradually be lost due to gravity if the trees that hold it are logged. This is soil erosion.
- Soil erosion can be prevented.

A. Fill in the blanks with the given words. Then draw lines to match the sentences with the correct pictures.

rain   waves   wind

Causes of Soil Erosion:

Soil can be washed away by heavy _____ . ◉

Soil can be blown away by strong _____ . ◉

Soil can be lost to the water by _____ . ◉

ISBN: 978-1-897164-31-0

B. **Match the methods of erosion prevention with the correct pictures. Write the letters.**

 A

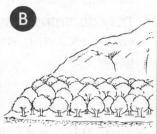 B

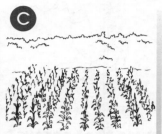 C

 D

Methods of Erosion Prevention:

1. Planting in tiers prevents soil loss by gravity. _____

2. Hedgerows prevent soil erosion by wind. _____

3. Cover crops protect soil by holding it with the roots of plants. _____

4. Replanting logged slopes prevents soil loss on mountainsides. _____

Experiment

Things needed:
- a sample of soil
- an old cake pan
- water

1. Pile the soil on one end of the pan so it looks like a miniature beach.
2. Slowly pour water into the other side of the pan – just enough to touch the beach.
3. Gently rock the pan so the water hits the soil like waves.

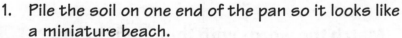

What happens to the soil?

Science Fact

When soil is repeatedly walked on, it compacts. Because little air is left in the soil, and water cannot be absorbed, plants cannot grow. What will happen next? With no plants and lots of feet: soil erosion.

ISBN: 978-1-897164-31-0

22

Earthworms

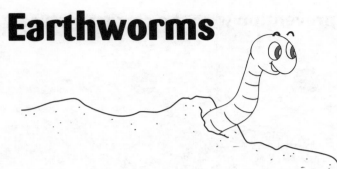

Importance of Earthworms to Soil:

- They mix up layers of soil and leave tunnels in the soil for air and water.
- They decompose dead leaves and animal waste, leaving nutrients for plants to grow well.

A.   Look at the picture that shows a worm's life underground. Fill in the boxes with the given words.

habitat   predator   food   tunnel   castings

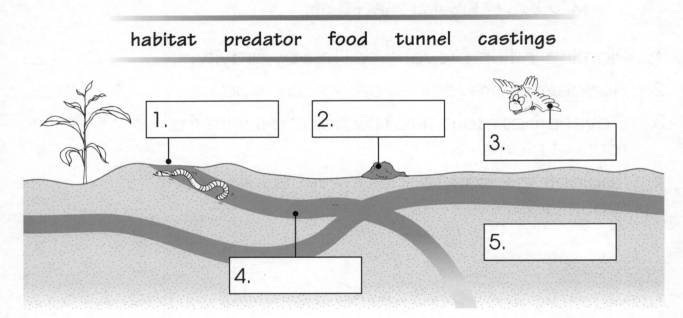

1.
2.
3.
4.
5.

B.   Match the words with their definitions.

1. Annelid   _____

2. Nocturnal   _____

3. Omnivorous   _____

4. Decomposer   _____

5. Castings   _____

A   eats both plants and animals or their wastes

B   helps break things down into smaller parts

C   the waste products of worms

D   active at night

E   a kind of animal that is divided into rings

ISBN: 978-1-897164-31-0

C. **Look at the picture. Fill in the blanks with the given words to complete the food chain.**

sun

leaf

human

small fish

big fish

worm

Food Chain

Science Fact

Ribbon worms are marine worms that can grow as long as 30 m.

ISBN: 978-1-897164-31-0

23

Creatures that Use Soil

We love clay.

- *People use soil for many different things.*
- *Soil is home to many animals.*

A. **People need soil for different things. Fill in the blanks with the given words to match the pictures.**

soil field   china
skin mud mask
flower pot of soil
clay brick   peat fuel

1

_____

2

_____

3

_____

4

_____

5

_____

House
under
Construction

6

_____

ISBN: 978-1-897164-31-0

B. **What animals live in soil? Use the picture clues and the given words to complete the puzzle.**

marmot   millipede   mite
nematode   pillbug   snail
ant   beetle   centipede
cicada   cricket   earwig

Science Fact

We can learn about the lives of ancient peoples through the discovery of buried pottery, such as clay pieces from thousands of years ago.

ISBN: 978-1-897164-31-0

Compost

- Composting is a process of decomposing plant and animal materials and happens naturally on the floor of every forest.
- We can make compost in our backyards with material from our gardens and kitchens.

Composting in Progress

A. Read the compost recipe. Then put a cross ✗ on the items that should not be put in the compost bin.

- **Items from garden**

- **Items from kitchen**

- **Items from other places**

Compost Recipe

- **Organic matter** *
- **Air**
- **Water**
- **Micro-organisms** **

* Use organic matter that was once alive and will break down easily, such as leaves and apple cores.

** Micro-organisms will add themselves to the compost pile – you cannot keep them away.

ISBN: 978-1-897164-31-0

B. Write "true" or "false" for each statement.

1. Compost needs air to decompose. _____

2. A compost pile can get very hot in the middle. _____

3. A compost pile should be kept dry. _____

4. Micro-organisms, or very tiny creatures, are responsible for decomposition. _____

5.

Meat and dairy products should not be composted as they attract rodents.

_____

C. Write the secret composting message on the line.

Com [ ] ing is a **1**derful way to re 🚲

organic 👁 tems.

Add finished compost to a vegetable or flower garden, or spread it under a tree.

_____

_____

Science Fact

People who don't have backyards can still compost. Red wiggler worms kept in a bin are happy to receive kitchen wastes. This is called vermicomposting.

ISBN: 978-1-897164-31-0

A. Tell what three things plants need. Label the parts of the plant. Then look at the diagram of a flower. Label the parts and answer the questions.

1. Plants need

   - _____
   - _____
   - _____

ovary   petal   pistil
sepal   stamen

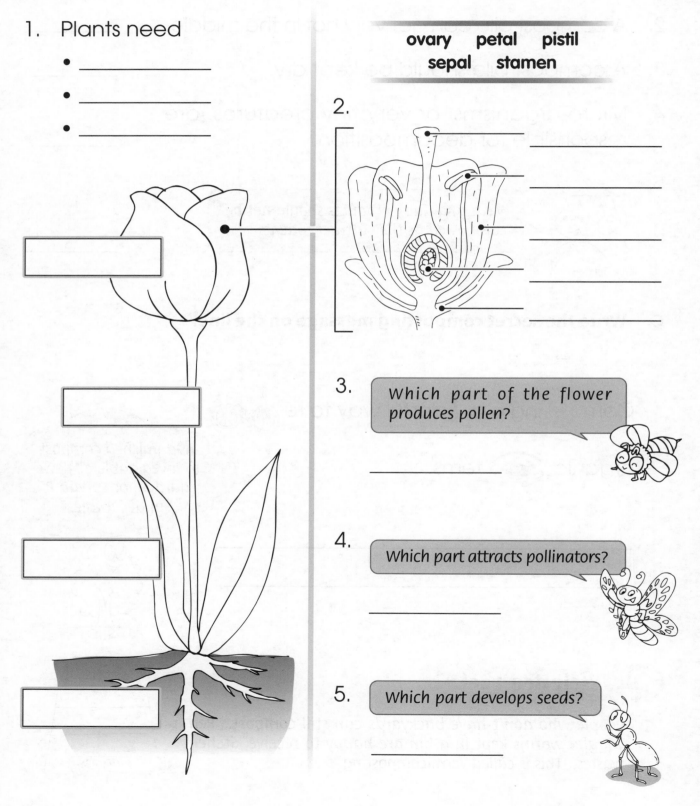

2.

3. Which part of the flower produces pollen?

   _____

4. Which part attracts pollinators?

   _____

5. Which part develops seeds?

   _____

ISBN: 978-1-897164-31-0

B. **Look at the flowers and the clues. Then tell what kind of pollination they use. Write the letters.**

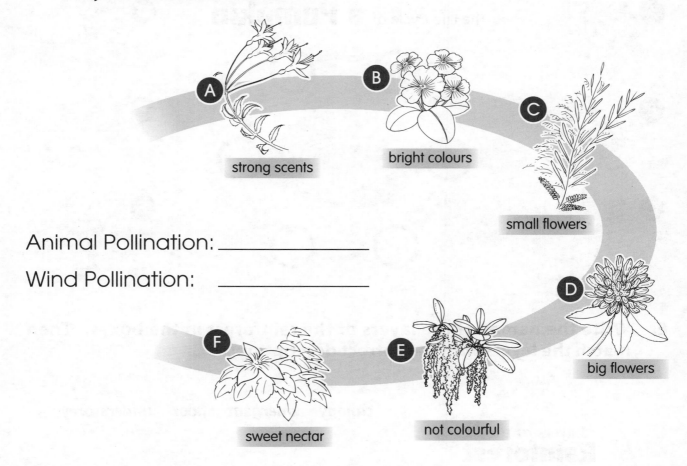

strong scents

bright colours

small flowers

big flowers

not colourful

sweet nectar

Animal Pollination: _____

Wind Pollination: _____

C. **Write what method each plant uses to disperse its seeds.**

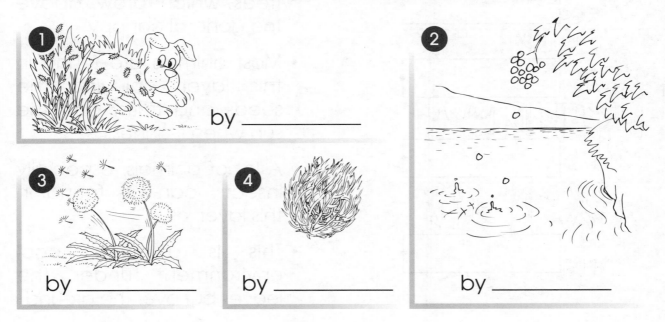

1 by _____

2 by _____

3 by _____

4 by _____

ISBN: 978-1-897164-31-0

D. **Put the pictures in the correct order to show the life cycle of a pumpkin.**

The Life Cycle of **a Pumpkin**

E. **Write the names of the layers of the rainforest in the boxes. Then match the layers with the correct descriptions.**

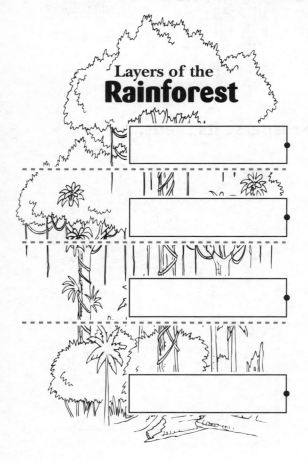

Layers of the **Rainforest**

canopy   emergent   floor   understorey

- This layer contains giant trees which grow above the general canopy.

- Most animals are found in this layer, enjoying the seeds and fruits, and the sun when it shines.

- A lot of animals, especially insects, can be found in this layer.

- This is a dark, cool environment under the leaves but over the ground.

ISBN: 978-1-897164-31-0

F. **Identify the types of forces in the pictures. Write "Push" or "Pull". Then describe the amount of friction. Write the correct words.**

1.

Type of force:

Force of friction: _____
small / great

2.

Type of force:

Force of friction: _____
small / great

G. **Fill in the blanks with the given words. Then draw lines from the magnetic objects to the horseshoe magnet.**

attracts   different   repels   same   south   north

Every magnet has a 1._____ pole and a 2._____ pole.

The north pole of one magnet 3._____ the south pole of

another magnet. 4._____ poles attract. The north pole of

one magnet 5._____ the north pole of

another magnet. 6._____ poles repel.

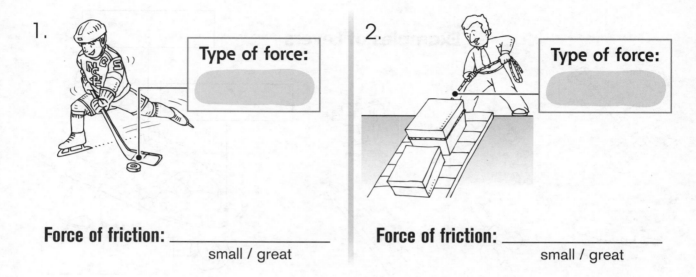

H. Check ✔ the tools that are levers. Then label the lever on the right with "fulcrum", "effort", and "load".

Examples of Levers

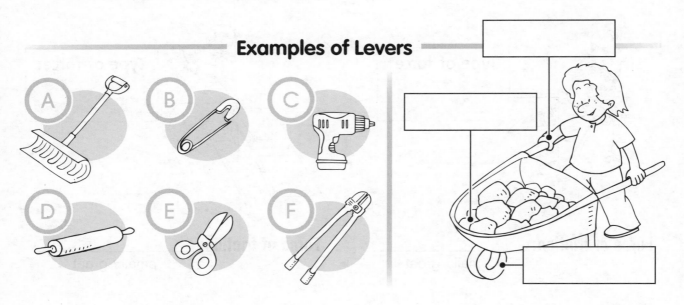

I. Write the names of the soil types. Then match them with the correct descriptions. Write the letters.

clay
sand
silt
loam

A Water drains easily from this soil.

B Plants grow well in this soil.

C This soil absorbs water well.

D This soil feels sticky and muddy.

Types of Soil
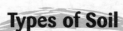

- _____ ; _____ : has the smallest rock particles

- _____ ; _____ : the size of the rock particles that are in between clay and sand

- _____ ; _____ : has the largest rock particles

- _____ ; _____ : a mixture of clay, silt, and sandy soil

ISBN: 978-1-897164-31-0

J. **Check ✔ the correct answers.**

1. The causes of soil erosion

   (A) by heavy rainfall   (B) by strong wind

   (C) by earthworms   (D) by waves

2. Things from soil

   (A) skin mud mask   (B) clay brick

   (C) peat fuel   (D) running shoes

3. Animals that live in soil

4. Things that can be put in a compost bin

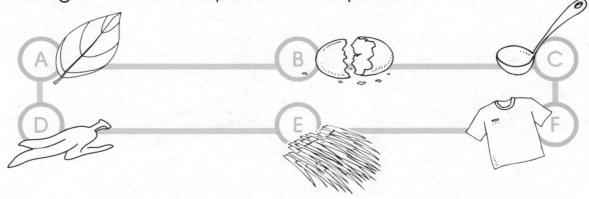

ISBN: 978-1-897164-31-0

ISBN: 978-1-897164-31-0

ANSWERS

ISBN: 978-1-897164-31-0

1   Numbers to 100

1. 37 ; 39 ; 40 ; 41 ; 43
2. 71 ; 72 ; 74 ; 75 ; 76
3. 89 ; 90 ; 91 ; 94 ; 95
4. 57 ; 59 ; 60 ; 61 ; 62
5. 49   6. 92   7. 70
8. 18, 39, 58, 63   9. 30, 44, 53, 81
10. 14, 16, 46, 64   11. forty-five
12. sixty-two   13. ninety-eight
14. 26   15. 45   16. 91
17. 80   18. 64   19. 38
20. 72   21. 53
22-25. (Suggested answers)
22. 66   23. 29   24. 10
25. 44
26.
75 70 65 60 55 50 45 40 35 30
27.
100 90 80 70 60 50 40 30 20 10
28.
88 86 84 82 80 78 76 74 72 70
29. 72 ; 66 ; 64 ; 60 ; 58
30. 80 ; 75 ; 65 ; 60 ; 55
31. 90 ; 80 ; 50 ; 40 ; 20
32. 34, 32, 30, 28 ; 2 ; 34
33. 60, 55, 50, 45 ; 5 ; 60
34.
50   60
50
35.
80   90
90
36.
60   70
70
37.
10   20
20
38. 84   39. 45 ; 54

2   Addition and Subtraction of 2-Digit Numbers

1. 53   2. 81   3. 81
4. 93   5. 87   6. 53
7. 80
8. 79 ;
$$\begin{array}{r} 50 \\ + 30 \\ \hline 80 \end{array}$$
9. 82 ;
$$\begin{array}{r} 20 \\ + 60 \\ \hline 80 \end{array}$$
10. 68 ;
$$\begin{array}{r} 10 \\ + 60 \\ \hline 70 \end{array}$$
11. 38 ;
$$\begin{array}{r} 10 \\ + 30 \\ \hline 40 \end{array}$$

12. A: 52   B: 23   C: 13
    D: 18   E: 35   F: 28
    G: 37   H: 6   I: 25
    J: 18
13. D and J   14. A
15. B
16. 35 ;
$$\begin{array}{r} 70 \\ - 40 \\ \hline 30 \end{array}$$
17. 27 ;
$$\begin{array}{r} 70 \\ - 40 \\ \hline 30 \end{array}$$
18. ✗ ; 49 ; 83
19. ✔ ;
$$\begin{array}{r} 45 \\ + 15 \\ \hline 60 \end{array}$$
20. 74 ;
$$\begin{array}{r} 16 \\ + 74 \\ \hline 90 \end{array}$$
21. 35 ;
$$\begin{array}{r} 24 \\ + 35 \\ \hline 59 \end{array}$$
22. 17 ;
$$\begin{array}{r} 16 \\ + 17 \\ \hline 33 \end{array}$$
23. 18 ;
$$\begin{array}{r} 66 \\ + 18 \\ \hline 84 \end{array}$$
24. a. 48 + 48 ; 96 ; 96
    b. 86 − 48 ; 38 ; 38
25. a. 42 − 36 ; 6 ; 6
    b. 36 + 42 ; 78 ; 78
26. a. 62 + 5 ; 67 ; 67
    b. 75 − 62 ; 13 ; 13

3   Numbers to 1000

1. 3 ; 5 ; 8 ; 358   2. 5 ; 4 ; 3 ; 543
3. 2 ; 9 ; 0 ; 290
4. A: 657   B: 524   C: 976
   D: 3 ; 7 ; 5   E: 5 hundreds 8 tens 1 one
5. 524, 581   6. 524, 581
7. 652, 625, 256   8. 887, 878, 788
9. 940, 904, 490   10. 423 ; 437 ; 449
11. 795 ; 821 ; 834
12. Mon: 645   Tue: 503   Wed: 296
13. Monday   14. 300
15. 500
16.
488 490 492 494 496 498 500 502   ; 2
17.
200 300 400 500 600 700 800 900   ; 100
18. 25 ; 550, 575, 600, 625, 650
19. 10 ; 750, 760, 770, 780, 790
20. 5 ; 715, 720, 725, 730, 735
21. 999 ; 100
22. 399, 400, 401, 402, 403
23. (Suggested answer)
    389, 390, 391, 392, 393
24. 6 ; 459, 495, 549, 594, 945, 954

ISBN: 978-1-897164-31-0

4 Addition and Subtraction of 3-Digit Numbers (1)

1. 339 2. 699 3. 495
4. 767 5. 568 6. 168
7. 836 8. 496 9. 398
10. 829
11. A: 448 B: 388
    C: 388 D: 497
    Answers greater than 450: D
    Answers smaller than 450: A, B, C

12. ①
   327
  +459
   786

13. ①
   436
  +127
   563

14. ①①
    85
  +516
   601

15. ①①
   652
  +149
   801

16. ①①
   584
  +266
   850

17. ①①
   298
  +298
   596

18. 446 19. 639 20. 822
21. 801 22. 494 23. 876
24. A: 537 B: 231 C: 490
    D: 555 E: 602 F: 251
    G: 318
    555 = D 251 = F
    231 = B 318 = G
25. 241 26. 421 27. 211
28. 309 29. 274 30. 338
31. 175 32. 221 33. 147
34. 249
35. A: 397 B: 236
    C: 142 D: 421
    D, A, B, C

36. a. 245 ; 418
    +173
    418

    b. 245 ; 72
    −173
    72

37. a. 318 ; 261
    − 57
    261

    b. 318 ; 579
    +261
    579

38. a. 362 ; 75
    −287
    75

    b. 362 ; 649
    +287
    649

5 Addition and Subtraction of 3-Digit Numbers (2)

1. 507 2. 750 3. 229
4. 585 5. 253 6. 907
7. 773 8. 123

9. 362 ; 162
      +362
      524

10. 46 ; 154
      + 46
      200

11. 232 ; 173
      +232
      405

12. 53 ; 318
      + 53
      371

13. 613 ; 400
      +200
      600

14. 798 ; 700
      +100
      800

15. 644 ; 800
      −200
      600

16. 258 ; 600
      −300
      300

17. 319 ; 319
    +254 −254
    573   65

18. 608 ; 608
    + 73 − 73
    681 535

19. 462 ; 462
    +353 −353
    815 109

20. 224 ; 537
    +537 −224
    761 313

21. 176 ; 413
    +413 −176
    589 237

22. 821 ; 821
    +117 −117
    938 704

23. a. 321 b. 237 24. a. 503 b. 276
25. a. 413 b. 165 26. a. 735 b. 188
27. A: 240 B: 590 C: 181
    B
28. A: 307 B: 601 C: 237
    C
29. 218 + 174 ; 392 ; 392
30. 182 + 203 ; 385 ; 385
31. 182 − 79 ; 103 ; 103
32. 203 − 174 ; 29 ; 29
33. 154 − 68 ; 86 ; 86

6 Length and Distance

1. m 2. km 3. cm
4. m 5. km 6. cm
7. m 8. cm 9. km
10. m 11. cm
12. (Individual estimates)
    A: 11 cm
    B: a bit shorter than 10 cm
    C: a bit longer than 7 cm
    D: a bit longer than 9 cm
13. 5 cm ; Draw a pencil which is about 7 cm long.
14. A: 3 cm ; B: 5 cm ; Draw a tree which is a bit shorter than 5 cm.
15. A: 11 cm B: 9 cm C: 11 cm
16. a. 65 b. 65 c. 50

ISBN: 978-1-897164-31-0

17 a. and 18 a.

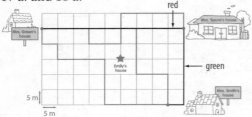

red

green

5 m

5 m

17. b. 45   18. b. 30

19. Mrs. Saura or Mrs. Smith

7   Perimeter and Area

1. 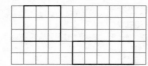   2.

3.

4. A: 12 cm   B: 14 cm   C: 10 cm
   D: 12 cm   E: 16 cm   F: 20 cm

5. (Individual estimates)
   Square: 16 cm   Hexagon : 22 cm
   Rectangle: 22 cm   Pentagon: 15 cm
   Triangle: 12 cm

6. (Suggested drawings)

7.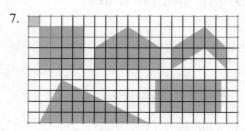

8. (Individual estimates)
   Square: 16   Pentagon: 18
   Hexagon: 10   Triangle: 20
   Rectangle: 18

9. the triangle

10. 8

---

11. (Suggested drawings)

12. 48 ; 12   13. smaller

14. 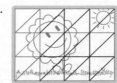 ; 24

8   Time and Temperature

1. 05 ; 5   2. 6 ; 7   3. 20 ; 20

4. A: 10:25 ; 25 min past 10
   B: 5:55 ; 5 min to 6
   C: 2:35 ; 25 min to 3
   D: 12:10 ; 10 min past 12
   E: 11:50 ; 10 min to 12

5. B ; A ; F ; D ; C ; E

6.

7. 39 ;   53
         − 14
            39

8. 13 ;   21
         −   8
            13

9. 12 ;   39
         − 27
            12

10. Sally

11. a.    12. a.

    b. B ; A   b. B ; A ; A

13.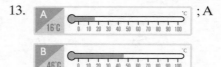

ISBN: 978-1-897164-31-0

9 Money

1.

2.

3.

4.

5. (Individual estimates)
   Jason: 9 ; 6
   Elaine: 8 dollars 69 cents
   Kevin: 7 dollars 50 cents
   Sally: 5 dollars 50 cents
   Bruce: 9 dollars

6. Jason   7. Sally

8. 4 ; 81 ; 4.81

9. 8 dollars 52 cents ; $8.52

10. 6 dollars 85 cents ; $6.85

11. 45 ; 2 ; 45 ; 2.45   12. 400 ; 4 ; 8 ; 4.08

13.

14.
| $5 | $2 | $2 |

25¢ 10¢ 1¢ 1¢ 1¢

15.
| $5 | $2 | $1 | 25¢ | 25¢ |

10¢ 10¢ 1¢ 1¢ 1¢ 1¢

16.
| $5 | $2 | $2 |

10¢ 5¢ 1¢

17.
| $5 | $1 |

25¢ 25¢ 25¢ 10¢ 5¢ 1¢ 1¢ 1¢

10 Addition and Subtraction with Money

1.
```
    3  21
 +  2  38
 ───────
    5  59
```

2.
```
    2  38
 +  3  27
 ───────
    5  65
```

3.
```
    3  21
 +  4  49
 ───────
    7  70
```

4.
```
    3  27
 +  4  49
 ───────
    7  76
```

5.
```
    2  38
 +  4  49
 ───────
    6  87
```

6.
```
    3  21
 +  3  27
 ───────
    6  48
```

7. C and D

8. 3.25 ;
```
    3  25 ;
 -  3  21
 ───────
       04
```
0.04

9. 4.30 ;
```
    4  30 ;
 -  3  27
 ───────
    1  03
```
1.03

10. 3.45 ;
```
    3  45 ;
 -  2  38
 ───────
    1  07
```
1.07

11. 6 ;
```
    5  100 ;
 -  4   49
 ────────
    1   51
```
1.51

12.
R & A Superstore	
Puzzle	$ 4.89
Crackers	$ 3.19
Total	$ 8.08
CASH	$ 10.00
CHANGE	$ 1.92

13.
R & A Superstore	
Detergent	$ 1.88
Bread	$ 2.16
Total	$ 4.04
CASH	$ 4.25
CHANGE	$ 0.21

14.
R & A Superstore	
Crackers	$ 3.19
Bread	$ 2.16
Total	$ 5.35
CASH	$ 6.00
CHANGE	$ 0.65

15.
R & A Superstore	
Detergent	$ 1.88
Detergent	$ 1.88
Total	$ 3.76
CASH	$ 5.00
CHANGE	$ 1.24

 ISBN: 978-1-897164-31-0

16.

R & A Superstore	
Bread	$ 2.16
Puzzle	$ 4.89
Total	$ 7.05
CASH	$ 7.25
CHANGE	$ 0.20

17.

R & A Superstore	
Crackers	$ 3.19
Detergent	$ 1.88
Total	$ 5.07
CASH	$10.00
CHANGE	$ 4.93

18. 1.23 ;
$$\begin{array}{r} 4\ 100 \\ -\ 3\ \ 77 \\ \hline 1\ \ 23 \end{array}$$

19. 2.17 ;
$$\begin{array}{r} 6\ 42 \\ -\ 4\ 25 \\ \hline 2\ 17 \end{array}$$

20. 7.32 ;
$$\begin{array}{r} 3\ 66 \\ +\ 3\ 66 \\ \hline 7\ 32 \end{array}$$

21. 8.91 ;
$$\begin{array}{r} 5\ 27 \\ +\ 3\ 64 \\ \hline 8\ 91 \end{array}$$

22. 4.77 + 4.77 = 9.54 ;
No, he needs 4¢ more.

11 Capacity and Mass

1. about 1 L: C ; F
   less than 1 L: B, D, E, G
   more than 1 L: A, H, I
2. H   3. E
4.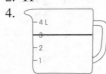
5.
6.
7. more than 200 L   8. about 100 L
9. less than 1 L
10. A: three quarters
    B: three quarters of a litre
    C: a quarter of a litre
    D: half a litre
11. a quarter ; 4   12. 50 L ; 25
13. Flour: 3 kg
    Pumpkin: 5 kg
    Rock: 8 kg
    Frog: 6 kg
    Watermelon: 5 kg
    Tin Soldier: 4 kg
14. pumpkin ; watermelon
15. 2
16.

17. A: three quarters
    B: a quarter of a kilogram
    C: half a kilogram
    D: three quarters of a kilogram
18. a. 4   b. 8   c. 2
19. a. 5   b. more   c. 8

12 Multiplication (1)

1.
3 + 3 + 3 ; 7 ; 7 ; 21

2.
4 + 4 + 4 + 4 + 4 ; 6 ; 4 ; 6 ; 4 ; 24

3.
5 + 5 + 5 + 5 + 5 ; 6 ; 5 ; 6 ; 5 ; 30

4. 4 ; 4 ; 4 ; 28   5. 5 ; 5 ; 5 ; 45
6. 5 ; 5 ; 5 ; 25   7. 8 ; 8 ; 8 ; 16
8. 4 ; 6 ; 24   9. 6 ; 3 ; 18
10. 5 ; 4 ; 20   11. 2 ; 8 ; 16
12.
3 6 9 12 15 18 21 24 27
13.
4 8 12 16 20 24 28 32 36
14.
7 14 21 28 35 42 49 56 63
15. 6 ; 12 ; 18 ; 24 ; 30 ; 36 ; 42 ; 48 ; 54
16. 2 ; 4 ; 6 ; 8 ; 10 ; 12 ; 14 ; 16 ; 18
17. 5 ; 10 ; 15 ; 20 ; 25 ; 30 ; 35 ; 40 ; 45
18.

X	1	2	3	4	5	6	7
1	1	2	3	4	5	6	7
2	2	4	6	8	10	12	14
3	3	6	9	12	15	18	21
4	4	8	12	16	20	24	28
5	5	10	15	20	25	30	35
6	6	12	18	24	30	36	42
7	7	14	21	28	35	42	49

ISBN: 978-1-897164-31-0

19. 24   20. 15   21. 14
22. 36   23. 20   24. 42
25. 24

13 Multiplication (2)

1. 27   2. 32   3. 30
4. 42   5. 14   6. 25
7. 24   8. 15   9. 24
10. 28   11. 45   12. 36
13. 48   14. 35   15. 8
16. 7   17. 3   18. 7

19. 24 ;
$$\begin{array}{r} 4 \\ \times\ 6 \\ \hline 24 \end{array}$$

20. 18 ;
$$\begin{array}{r} 6 \\ \times\ 3 \\ \hline 18 \end{array}$$

21. 28 ;
$$\begin{array}{r} 7 \\ \times\ 4 \\ \hline 28 \end{array}$$

22. 6 key chains ;
$$\begin{array}{r} 7 \\ \times\ 5 \\ \hline 35 \end{array} \quad \begin{array}{r} 6 \\ \times\ 6 \\ \hline 36 \end{array}$$

23. a.
$$\begin{array}{r} 4 \\ \times\ 4 \\ \hline 16 \end{array}$$; 16
  b.
$$\begin{array}{r} 7 \\ \times\ 4 \\ \hline 28 \end{array}$$; 28

24. a.
$$\begin{array}{r} 6 \\ \times\ 3 \\ \hline 18 \end{array}$$; 18
  b.
$$\begin{array}{r} 5 \\ \times\ 6 \\ \hline 30 \end{array}$$; 30

25. a.
$$\begin{array}{r} 6 \\ \times\ 5 \\ \hline 30 \end{array}$$; 30
  b.
$$\begin{array}{r} 2 \\ \times\ 7 \\ \hline 14 \end{array}$$; 14

26. Tina: 28 ; 8 ; 36
    Eva: 10 ; 16 ; 26
    Susan: 35 ; 5 ; 40
27. Susan   28. Eva
29. No   30. 18

14 Division (1)

1. ; 15 ; 5

2.  ; 21 ; 3

3. ; 20 ; 4

4.  ; 7

5.  ; 2

6. ; 3

7. ; 6

8. 6 ;

9. 7 ;

10. 5 ;

11. 3 ;

12. a. 15   b. 3   c. 5
13. a. 24   b. 3   c. 6
14. A

Review 1

1. a. A: 42   B: 47   C: 55
  b. 47
  c. 65

ISBN: 978-1-897164-31-0

2. a. D: 691   E: 699   F: 708
    b. 699
    c. 591
3. 29   4. 74   5. 352
6. 714   7. 4 ; 3 ; 9   8. 5 ; 8 ; 6
9. 65   10. 25   11. 71
12. 583   13. 226   14. 303
15. 520   16. 17   17. 117
18. 620   19. 266   20. 48
21. 462 − 384 ; 78 ; 78
22. 462 + 384 ; 846 ; 846
23. 462 + 462 ; 924 ; 924
24. 924 − 110 ; 814 ; 814
25. 55 ;   279   26. 309 ;   108
         + 55   + 309
          334   417

27. 137 ;   463   28. 8 ;   795
          + 137   +   8
           600   803

29. A: shorter ; 12 cm
    B: 14 cm
    C: longer ; 13 cm
30. B
31. Draw a pencil which is about 11 cm long.
32. 12   33. 28
34. 6   35. 7
36. A: 4:10   B: 4:35   C: 4:51
37. 25 ;   35   38. 16 ;   51
          − 10   − 35
           25   16

39. 7.97 ; 7 ; 97
40. 6.41 ; 6 ; 41
41.   7 97 ;   42.   6 100 ;
      + 7 97   − 6   41
       15 94   59

    15.94   0.59

43-44. (Suggested drawings)
43.   44.

   1 L   1 L

45. 27   46. 32   47. 49
48. 12   49. 28   50. 15
51. 20   52. 18   53. 56
54. 5 x 6 ; 30 ; 30   55. 9 x 7 ; 63 ; 63

56. ☺ ☺ ☺ ☺ ;   57. ☺ ☺ ☺ ;
     ☺ ☺ ☺ ☺   ☺ ☺ ☺
     ☺ ☺ ☺ ☺   ☺ ☺ ☺
     ☺ ☺ ☺ ☺   ☺ ☺ ☺
     ☺ ☺ ☺ ☺   ☺ ☺ ☺
     ☺ ☺ ☺ ☺   ☺ ☺ ☺
     ☺ ☺ ☺ ☺

     4   6

15 Division (2)

1. 5 ; 5   2. 3 ; 3   3. 4 ; 4
4. 6 ;   6   5. 4 ;   4
        3)18   5)20
           18   20

6.   6   7.   3
     5)30   8)24
        30   24

8.   8   9.   6
     2)16   7)42
        16   42

10. 5   11. 5   12. 4
13. 3   14. 3   15. 7
16. 5   17. 7   18. 5
19. 9 ;   9   20. 8 ;   8
        3)27   2)16
           27   16

21. 6 ;   6
        5)30
           30

22.   3 R 3   23.   6 R 2
      4)15   3)20
        12   18
         3   2

24.   2 R 4
      7)18
        14
         4

25. 2R1   26. 3R1
27. 4R2   28. 4R2
29. 25 ; 7 ; 3R4 ; 3 ; 4   30. 26 ; 3 ; 8R2 ; 8 ; 2

16 Multiplication and Division

1. 18   2. 36
3. 35   4. 16
5.   5   6.   8 R 1
     8)40   5)41
        40   40
                                1

ISBN: 978-1-897164-31-0

7.
```
    4
6 ) 24
    24
```

8.
```
    9
4 ) 36
    36
```

9.
```
    6
7 ) 42
    42
```

10.
```
    6 R 2
3 ) 20
    18
     2
```

11. 8   12. 36   13. 3R3
14. 4   15. 15   16. 48
17. 27   18. 8

19-22. (Suggested answers)

19. 3 ; 6 ; 18 ;
    18 ; 3 ; 6

20. 2 ; 8 ; 16 ;
    16 ; 2 ; 8

21. 4 ; 7 ; 28 ;
    28 ; 4 ; 7

22. 5 ; 4 ; 20 ;
    20 ; 5 ; 4

23-26. (Suggested answers)

23. 3 x 5 = 15
    15 ÷ 3 = 5

24. 4 x 6 = 24
    24 ÷ 4 = 6

25. 3 x 9 = 27
    27 ÷ 3 = 9

26. 4 x 7 = 28
    28 ÷ 4 = 7

27. B ; 28 ; 28   28. A ; 4 ; 4
29. C ; 48 ; 48   30. D ; 8 ; 8

31. 32 ;
```
      4
    x 8
     32
```

32. 4 ;
```
    4
7 ) 28
    28
```

33. 9 ;
```
    9
3 ) 27
    27
```

34. 7 x 5 ; 35 ; 35
35. 49 ÷ 5 ; 9R4 ; 10

17 Fractions

1. ;
   eighths

2. ;
   sixths

3.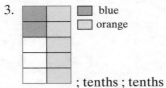
   ■ blue
   □ orange
   ; tenths ; tenths

4. five   5. three sevenths
6. one fourth   7. five sixteenths
8. five tenths   9. four ninths
10. two fifths   11. three fourths
12. five sixths   13. four ninths

14. ; eighths

15. 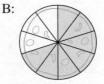 ; Two ; sixths

16. ; Four ; fifths

17. ☆ ☆ ☆ ☆ ☆ ; Two ; thirds
    ☆ ☆ ☆ ☆ ☆
    ☆ ☆ ☆ ☆ ☆

18. ▦ ; ▥ ; three fifths

19. ▦ ; ▥ ; two fourths

20. △ ; △ ; two thirds

21. ⬤ ; ⬤ ; five sixths

22. A: ▦   B: ▥
    C: ▦
    B ; A ; C

23. A: 🍕   B: 🍕
    C: 🍕
    A ; C ; B

18 2-D Shapes (1)

1. Colour the shapes: A, C, D, E, F, G, H.
   A: triangle   C: pentagon   D: hexagon
   E: rectangle   F: heptagon   G: pentagon
   H: octagon
2. Irregular: A, C, E
   Regular: D, F, G, H
3. 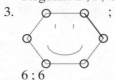 ;   4. ;
   6 ; 6   4 ; 4
5. 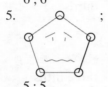 ;   6. 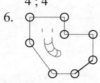 ;
   5 ; 5   8 ; 8
7. ;   8. 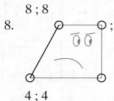 ;
   4 ; 4   4 ; 4
9. ✘ ; 5   10. ✘ ; square / rhombus
11. ✔   12. ✔
13. Check the pictures: B, E, F.
14. 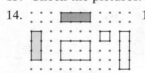 15.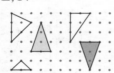
16. 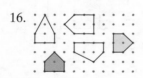 17.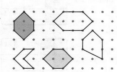
18. 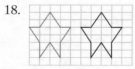 19.
20. Square:
    side length longer than 2 cm: A, D
    side length shorter than 2 cm: I
    Pentagon:
    side length longer than 2 cm: F
    side length shorter than 2 cm: E
    Hexagon:
    side length longer than 2 cm: C
    side length shorter than 2 cm: B, G, H

19 2-D Shapes (2)

1.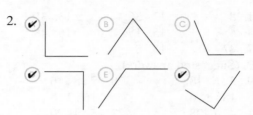
2.

   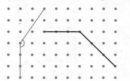
3-6. (Suggested drawings)
   3. greater than a right angle

   4. a right angle

   5. smaller than a right angle

   6. greater than a right angle

7.   8.

9.   10.

● red   ● yellow   ● blue

ISBN: 978-1-897164-31-0

11.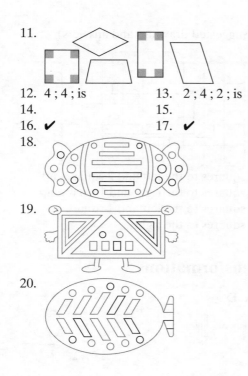

12. 4 ; 4 ; is   13. 2 ; 4 ; 2 ; is
14.   15.
16. ✔   17. ✔
18.

19.

20.

20 3-D Figures (1)

1. A: 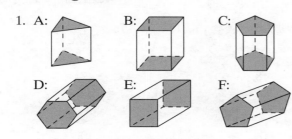 B: C:

   D: E: F:

   A: triangle ; triangular prism
   B: rectangle ; rectangular prism
   C: pentagon ; pentagonal prism
   D: hexagon ; hexagonal prism
   E: square ; square-based prism
   F: pentagon ; pentagonal prism

2.   3.

   rectangle ;   triangle ;
   rectangular pyramid triangular pyramid

4.   5.

   hexagon ;   pentagon ;
   hexagonal pyramid pentagonal pyramid

6.    7.

   square ;   hexagon ;
   square-based pyramid hexagonal pyramid

8. A: ;   B: ;

   6 ; 12 ; 8   4 ; 6 ; 4

   C: 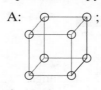 ;   D: 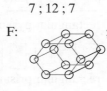 ;

   6 ; 10 ; 6   7 ; 12 ; 7

   E: ;   F: ;

   5 ; 9 ; 6   8 ; 18 ; 12

9. B ; A, C, D, E, F   10. B, C, E ; A, D, F
11. B ; A, C, D, E, F
12. hexagonal prism   13. pentagonal pyramid
14. rectangular prism   15. triangular pyramid
16. D   17. C
18. A, C

21 3-D Figures (2)

1. Colour the nets: A, C, D, G.
2. 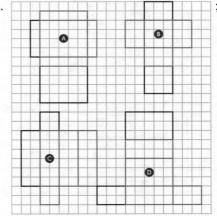 ;

   C ; D ; B ; A

ISBN: 978-1-897164-31-0

3. A:
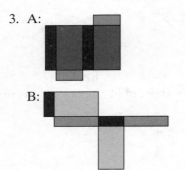

   B:

4. 6   5. rectangle
6. 3
7. rectangle ; triangle
8. hexagon ; rectangle
9. pentagon ; triangle
10. rectangle ; square
11.

rectangular pyramid ; 4 ; 1

12.

rectangular prism ; 6

13.

hexagonal prism ; 2 ; 6

14. A, C   15. A, B

22 Locations of Shapes and Objects

1. 5   2. 4   3. 5
4. 3   5. 4 ; 3   6. 2 ; 5

7-9.

10. 1
11.
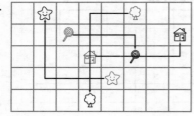

12-15. (Suggested drawings and answers)
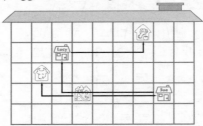

12. 5 squares to the left and 2 squares up
13. 4 squares to the right and 1 square up
14. 2 squares to the left and 1 square up
15. 4 squares to the right

23 Transformations

1. A, D
2.   3.
4.   5.
6.   7.
8.   9.
10.   11.
12.   13.
14. A, C   15. A, B   16. B, C
17. 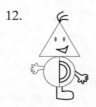   18.   19.

ISBN: 978-1-897164-31-0

20. slide   21. turn   22. flip
23. slide   24. turn   25. flip
26. flip

24 Patterns (1)

1.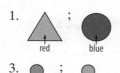
   red   blue

2. ;
   green   blue

3.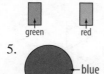
   green   red

4.
   yellow   yellow

5.
   — blue

2 ; 2 ; sizes

6.
   ← yellow

2 ; rectangle ; 2 ; orientations

7. 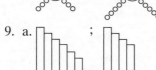 ; 2 ; 2 ; hexagon ; pentagon
   ← blue

8. a.    b. growing

9. a. 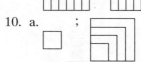   b. shrinking

10. a.   b. growing

11. 30 ; 35 ; growing   12. 15 ; 12 ; shrinking
13. 50 ; 40 ; shrinking
14 and 17.

1	2	3	4	5	6	7	8	9	10
11	12	13	14	15	16	17	18	19	20
21	22	23	24	25	26	27	28	29	30
31	32	33	34	35	36	37	38	39	40
41	42	43	44	45	46	47	48	49	50
51	52	53	54	55	56	57	58	59	60
61	62	63	64	65	66	67	68	69	70
71	72	73	74	75	76	77	78	79	80
81	82	83	84	85	86	87	88	89	90
91	92	93	94	95	96	97	98	99	100

15. diagonally   16. in columns
18. Yes

25 Patterns (2)

1. 7 ; 14 ; 21 ; 28 ; 35 ; 42 ; 49 ; 56
2. 39 ; 36 ; 33 ; 30 ; 27 ; 24 ; 21 ; 18
3. 24 ; 28 ; 32 ; 36 ; 40 ; 44 ; 48 ; 52
4. 35 ; 30 ; 25 ; 20 ; 15 ; 10 ; 5 ; 0
5. 24 ; 30 ; 36 ; 42 ; 48 ; 54 ; 60
6. 80 ; 72 ; 64 ; 56 ; 48 ; 40 ; 32
7. a.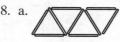
   b. 4 ; 7 ; 10 ; 13   c. 19
8. a.
   b. 3 ; 5 ; 7 ; 9   c. 13
9. a.
   b. 54 ; 40 ; 28 ; 18   c. 10

10. 7   11. 20   12. 8
13. 19   14. 9   15. 12
16. 7   17. 21   18. 16
19. 25   20. 3   21. 12
22. 18   23. 5   24. 6
25. 30   26. 17   27. 4

28. ♡ + 4 = 9   29. ☆ − 4 = 19
    ♡ = 5   ☆ = 23

30. 15 = 21 − ☀   31. ☽ − 6 = 23
    ☀ = 6   ☽ = 29

32. 17 = 27 − 🍎   33. 15 = 10 + ⊙
    🍎 = 10   ⊙ = 5

34. 21 = 22 − 🐱
    🐱 = 1

26 Graphs (1)

1. 4   2. 105   3. 75
4. 10   5. 660   6. 40
7. 90   8. 120   9. 320
10. "The sport car" had the greatest sale because the number of sport cars left is the smallest.
11. (Suggested answer)
    He should promote the "Octopus" because he has the most "Octopus" in stock.

12.

Flower buttons with 4 holes	Flower buttons with 2 holes	Square buttons with 4 holes	Square buttons with 2 holes
⊞⊞ ⊞⊞ ⊞⊞ ⊞⊞ ⊞⊞⊞⊞	⊞⊞ ⊞⊞	⊞⊞ ⊞⊞ ⊞⊞ ⊞⊞ ⊞⊞ ⊞⊞	⊞⊞ ⊞⊞ ⊞⊞ ⊞⊞⊞⊞

13.

Judy's Buttons

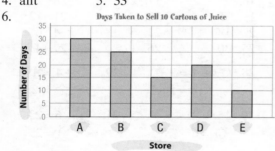

Flower buttons with 4 holes	Flower buttons with 2 holes	Square buttons with 4 holes	Square buttons with 2 holes

14. 34   15. 88   16. 51

27 Graphs (2)

1. 8   2. 5   3. ladybug
4. ant   5. 33
6.

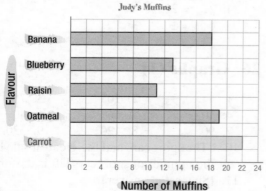

7. Days Taken to Sell 10 Cartons of Juice
8. 5   9. A and B   10. E ; 1
11.

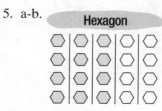

12. 5   13. 42   14. 83
15. 83   16. 108 cm   17. 58 kg
18. 70 cm   19. $275

28 Probability

1. B   2. C
3. a. Apple, orange, or strawberry
   b. No
4. (Suggested answer)
   26 ; 12 ; 12
5. Happy face, flower, tree, or sun
6. Happy face : 10   Flower : 10
   Tree : 15   Sun : 5
7. B, D, E, F
8-9. (Individual colouring)
8.   9.

10. a. No
    b. No ; take out 1 star marble.
11. a. Yes
    b. Cross out any 3 letter marbles and 1 shape
       marble.
12. (Suggested answer)

Review 2

1. a. $4\overline{)20}$ $\dfrac{5}{}$ $\underline{20}$
   b. $6\overline{)20}$ 3 R 2 $\underline{18}$ 2

2. a. $3\overline{)15}$ $\dfrac{5}{}$ $\underline{15}$
   b. $4\overline{)15}$ 3 R 3 $\underline{12}$ 3

3. a. 8 x 5 ; 40 ; 40   b. 28 ÷ 5 ; 5R3 ; 5
4. a. 48 ÷ 6 ; 8 ; 8   b. 9 x 3 ; 27 ; 27
5. a-b.

Hexagon

c. Three fifths

ISBN: 978-1-897164-31-0

6. a-b.

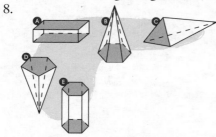

c. Three fourths

7. greater than a right angle: C, G
   a right angle: A, E
   smaller than a right angle: B, D, F, H

8.

A: rectangle ; rectangular prism
B: hexagon ; hexagonal pyramid
C: triangle ; triangular pyramid
D: pentagon ; pentagonal pyramid
E: hexagon ; hexagonal prism

9. 6   10. 10   11. A, E

12. A, E

13.

14.

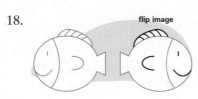

15. 5 squares to the left and 2 squares up

16. 3 squares to the right and 2 squares up

17.

18.

19. a.

b. 3 ; hexagon ; 2 ; orientations

20. a.

b. 2 ; heart ; 2 ; sizes

21. 100000 ; 1000000 ; growing

22. 44 ; 4 ; shrinking

23.

Number of Balloons Sold Yesterday

Colour	Number of Balloons
Blue	19
Green	15
Yellow	20
Red	18

0 2 4 6 8 10 12 14 16 18 20 22

Number of Balloons

24. 3   25. 72   26. C, D

ISBN: 978-1-897164-31-0

1 Groundhog Day

A. 1. B   2. A
   3. C   4. D

B. (Individual drawing and writing)

C. 1. s   2. h
   3. w   4. t
   5. l   6. k
   7. b   8. gh

D. 1. The knight was frightened by the lightning last night.
   2. Don't write the answers in the wrong column.
   3. He designed eight Christmas cards.
   4. The scientist stayed calm when he saw the ghost.
   5. The rhino is blowing a whistle beside the lamb.

E. (Individual answers)

2 The New Student

A. B

B. 1. No
   2. Yes
   3. No
   4. No
   5. Yes
   6. No
   7. Yes

C. Hard "C": A ; B ; C ; F ; H
   Soft "C": A ; D ; E ; G

D.
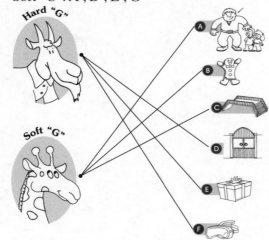

3 Acrostic Poems

A. (Individual drawing)
   1. Rainbow
   2. Mother

B. (Individual writing)

C.

D. (Colour the pictures of 1, 2, 5, 6, 7, and 9.)

4 What Are Things Made of?

A. 1. G   2. A
   3. H   4. E
   5. F   6. D
   7. B   8. C

B. 1. grow
   2. soil
   3. touch
   4. plants
   5. world
   6. things

C. 1. train
   2. day
   3. eight
   4. eat
   5. tree
   6. load
   7. know
   8. boot

ISBN: 978-1-897164-31-0

9. crew
10. cause
11. jaw

D. 1. 2.
   3. 4. ✘
   5. ✘ 6.
   7. ✘ 8. ✘

5 A Special Gym Class

A.

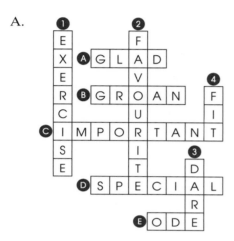

B. (Individual writing)
C. (Cross out these words.)
   1. school
   2. player
   3. tail
   4. efforts
   5. fast
   6. peaches
D. (Individual new rhyming words)
   1. C 2. A
   3. G 4. B
   5. F 6. D
   7. E

6 The Frank Slide

A. 1. 2. ✔
   3. 4.
   5. ✔ 6. ✔
B. 1. C 2. B
   3. F 4. A
   5. E 6. D
C. 1. Aunt Rosaline and her family moved to Edmonton last year.
   2. Her daughter Sherry told me that West Edmonton Mall is the world's largest shopping centre.
   3. You can find all types of shops in the mall.
   4. Have you ever heard of Turtle Mountain?
   5. There was a town called Frank at the foot of the mountain.
   6. Alberta is a province to the east of British Columbia.
   7. My family will take a trip to Banff next month.
   8. Our neighbour will take care of our dog Mickey for us.
D. (Individual answers)

7 A Gaggle of Geese?

A. 1. cattle
   2. fish
   3. penguins
   4. crows
   5. wolves
   6. lions
   7. sheep
   8. kittens
   9. geese
   10. seals
B. (Individual drawing and title)
C. 1. feet
   2. deer
   3. cities
   4. mice

ISBN: 978-1-897164-31-0

5. knives
6. families
7. teeth
8. leaves
9. offspring

D.

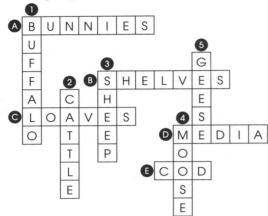

8 The Goat – Our Best Friend

A. 1. doe / nanny
2. kid
3. buck / billy
B. 1. wool ; clothing
2. meat
3. leather ; gloves ; boots
4. milk ; feta
C. 1. . ; T
2. ? ; A
3. . ; I
4. ! ; S
5. ? ; A
6. . ; T
7. ! ; S
8. . ; I
9. ? ; A
10. . ; T
D. (Individual writing)

9 The Narwhal

A. 1. lucky
2. sure
3. tusk
4. amazing
5. real
6. whales
7. twists
8. blotches
B. 1. five metres
2. blue-grey
3. white blotches
4. brown
5. Canada
6. other northern countries
7. using sound waves
C. 1. My class|is doing a project on the narwhal.
2. Mrs. Reid|told us to look for information about the narwhal on the Internet.
3. The narwhal|is a whale.
4. The left tooth of the male narwhal|can grow up to three metres long.
5. The female|is slightly smaller than the male.
6. The skin of a baby narwhal|is brown in colour.
7. You|may see a narwhal in the Arctic seas.
8. Fish, squid, and shrimps|are what narwhals eat.
9. I|think a narwhal really looks like a unicorn.
D. 1. Our teacher
2. The main character
3. Bruce
4. The unicorn
5. The fairy tale
6. We
E. (Individual writing)

ISBN: 978-1-897164-31-0

10 Skipping Rope

A.

```
a J e s p b a n a n a s J p a c
p a C F e b r u a r y b a l p p
p n e M a c u m p l M a n u F l
e o a n c s a s p e a n u S e u
  k c y h e r p l u m s a e o
    h F e d y l e p M a r c h
    a s f t u s e a e y s
```

B. 1. exercise
    2. friends
    3. chant
    4. skipper
    5. caught

C. 1. There are four seasons in Canada. They are
       spring, summer, fall, and winter.
    2. June, July, and August are the summer months
       in Ontario.
    3. I like skipping, swimming, cycling, and rock
       climbing.
    4. Sarah asked, "Would you like to skip with
       me?"
    5. "Let's ask Jerry to join us," I said.
    6. She reminded me, "Don't forget to take your
       skipping rope with you."
    7. We sell all kinds of fruits: apples, oranges,
       bananas, peaches, cherries, mangoes – you
       name it.

D. 1. ✔
    2.
    3. ✔
    4.
    5. ✔
    6. ✔
    7.

11 I Love Haiku!

A. 1.
    2.
    3. ✔
B. 1. poems

2. short
3. three
4. Japan
5. frog

C. 1. 3
    2. 4
    3. 2
    4. 2
    5. 1
    6. 4
    7. 3
    8. 1
    9. 4

D. 1 Syllable: sound ; book ; bright
    2 Syllables: famous ; pizza ; author
    3 Syllables: acrostic ; Japanese ; lollipop
    4 Syllables: competition ; information ; stationery

E. 1. s y l / l a / b l e
    2. g a r / a g e
    3. a f / t e r / n o o n
    4. c o l / o u r / f u l
    5. c a r / r y
    6. e x / c i t / i n g
    7. i n / v i s / i / b l e
    8. n e / c e s / s a / r y

12 Why Do We Sneeze?

A.

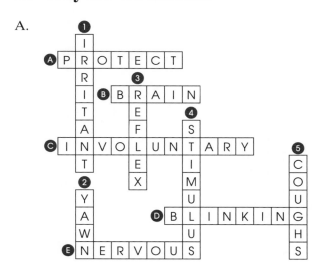

B.   1. They
2. We
3. It
4. He
5. You
6. She
7. I

C.   1. me
2. them
3. you
4. ✔
5. ✔
6. him
7. us

D.   1. our
2. My
3. Her
4. his
5. its
6. their
7. your

13   Girl's Festival in Japan

A.

B.

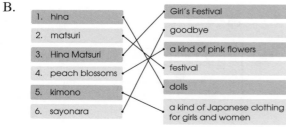

C.   1. Girl's
2. Kiyoka's
3. grandma's
4. dolls'
5. sister's
6. friends'
7. Tanaka's
8. daughter's

14   A Visit to the Seniors' Centre

A.   D ; B ; A ; C ; E

B.   1. She asked the writer to do a project about his favourite fish.
2. Some of the old people could not hear very well.
3. He thought that the people at the seniors' centre were very interesting and kind to him.

C.   1. this
2. That
3. those
4. This
5. that
6. These

D.   1. This book is mine.
2. These stickers are his.
3. Is this lunch box yours?
4. Those shoes are hers.
5. That puppy is ours.
6. These pictures are theirs.

Review 1

A.   1. knight
2. cow
3. bow
4. castle
5. chain
6. comb
7. feather
8. beetle

ISBN: 978-1-897164-31-0

B. With a Hard "C" Sound: carpet ; cookie ; cycle ; candle

With a Soft "C" Sound: cycle ; citizen ; cent
With a Hard "G" Sound: goose ; garage ; golf
With a Soft "G" Sound: gypsy ; garage ; gem
"Y" with a Long "E" Sound: baby ; gypsy ; puppy
"Y" with a Long "I" Sound: rhyme ; hyphen ; cycle

C.

luggages (foots (

information ④   advices (

media ③   salmon ②   carries (

halves ①   receives (babys (

rhino ②   blueberries ③   elfs (

furnitures (evidence ③

D. (Suggested answers)
1. gate
2. beans
3. pie
4. beet
5. jug
6. pen
7. mall
8. Sticks
9. dog

E. 1. "Don't forget to turn off the light," Mom reminded me.
2. "This is the core part of the computer," said Brian.
3. Miss Hall said, "You'll need a balloon, a marker, and some buttons."
4. "We'll go to Lake Simcoe, Niagara Falls, or Wasaga Beach this weekend," Dad told us.

5. Moose, hippos, cheetahs, and black bears are some of the animals you can see at the zoo.
6. "I'd like to join you," said Anne, Jimmy, and Lester together.
7. The government encourages all office buildings to "go green" to protect the environment.

F. 1. her
2. Mr. and Mrs. Alden's
This picture is theirs.
3. These are his marbles.
These marbles are his.
(Individual writing of the wish)

15 A Letter to – and from – Ms. Naughton

A. 1. doing volunteer work at the hospital twice a week
2. going for a long walk every day
3. working at the library
4. writing a book about being a principal for 30 years
5. learning to play golf
B. (Individual writing)
C. 1. helps
2. invites
3. wear
4. use ; read
5. asks
6. choose ; put
7. are
D. 1. ✔
2. goes
3. is
4. ✔
5. enjoy
E. 1. The kittens drink the milk happily.
2. The children are looking at the ladybug.
3. The pastries taste sweet and delicious.
4. The girls put away their books.

16 The Sugar Shack

A.
 baked beans
 bacon
 sausages
 ham
 corned beef
 fried eggs
 waffles
 pancakes
 scrambled eggs

B.
1. little
2. right
3. perfect
4. done
5. collected
6. way
7. buckets
8. outdoors
9. delicious

C.

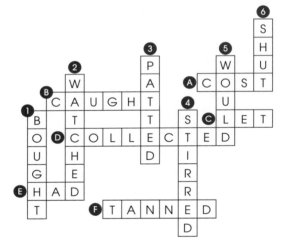

D.
1. promised
2. hurried
3. arrived
4. were
5. grabbed
6. bought
7. poured

8. did
9. spread
10. devoured
11. ate
12. choked
13. looked
14. knew
15. was
16. burst

17 The Amazing Coconut

A.

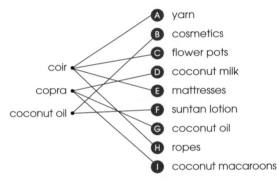

B.
1. Add boiling water to dried coconut.
2. Blend / Put it in the blender.
3. Strain out the bits.

C.
1. amazing
2. white ; large ; hard
3. young ; green ; tender
4. healthy ; refreshing
5. useful
6. strong
7. brown ; tough
8. dried ; shredded ; delicious

D.
1. big ; tall
2. slimy ; wet
3. bright ; cold
4. Colourful ; early
5. stuffy ; crowded

E. (Individual writing)

ISBN: 978-1-897164-31-0

18 Shooting Stars

A.

q	m	E	a	r	h	e	c	i	d	h	m	e	t	o	l
m	e	t	e	o	r	s	o	q	c	r	e	c	k	j	b
o	r	d	s	c	k	p	n	s	h	a	t	n	a	s	p
h	o	e	t	k	E	a	r	t	h	E	e	h	o	c	f
j	k	a	r	s	p	c	s	r	n	a	o	s	m	e	d
l	e	m	e	c	o	n	c	e	n	t	r	a	t	e	g
s	p	a	o	e	c	t	i	a	z	g	i	c	o	t	k
h	t	z	b	a	e	s	v	k	l	r	t	e	i	r	p
b	c	i	s	g	t	p	g	h	a	m	e	t	t	e	o
r	o	n	s	t	r	a	q	j	w	i	s	h	o	c	m
e	n	g	i	p	m	c	o	n	c	t	r	o	c	s	f
n	t	k	d	i	E	e	a	t	h	p	h	t	i	k	j
i	s	t	a	e	k	n	b	a	m	a	s	e	l	g	c

B.
1. ✔
2. ✔
3.
4. ✔
5. ✔
6.
7. ✔
8. ✔

C.
1. eagerly
2. patiently
3. high
4. late
5. gracefully

D. (Individual writing)

19 The Circus School

A.
2. nutrition class
3. French class
4. music and rhythm class
5. balancing class
6. acrobatics class
7. aerials class
8. clowning arts class

B. (Individual writing)

C. on chairs
   in the sky

inside the box
at sunset
beside the doll
at Christmas
behind the house
at two o'clock
in the morning
on weekends
in 2006
above Lydia

Where: on chairs ; in the sky ; inside the box ; beside the doll ; behind the house ; above Lydia

When: at sunset ; at Christmas ; at two o'clock ; in the morning ; on weekends ; in 2006

D.
1. On
2. at
3. on
4. in
5. in
6. under
7. inside
8. in
9. at
10. on
11. in

20 My Brother Loves to Dance

A.
1. B
2. C
3. C
4. A
5. B

B.
1. Toller has won many awards.
2. The writer's father / Toller's father pretended to be Morris in the role play.
3. Everyone cheered when Toller finished his dance.

C.
1. didn't
2. I've
3. doesn't
4. there's
5. she's
6. we'll
7. shouldn't
8. he'd

D. 1. didn't
   2. couldn't
   3. hadn't
   4. He'll
   5. He'd
E. 1. Mr.
   2. km
   3. Blvd.
   4. Nov.
   5. no.
   6. B.C.
   7. Mt.
F. 1. Toller will join a dance competition in Oct.
   2. It will take place in a school on Berry Dr.
   3. He will go on a trip to P.E.I. afterwards.

21 Lacrosse

A. 4 ; 2 ; 3 ; 1
B. 1. F   2. F
   3. F   4. T
   5. T   6. T
   7. F   8. T
C. (Cross out these words.)
   Re: result ; reach ; retrieve ; repeat
   Un: under ; unit ; unless ; uncle
D. 1. unpopular
   2. redevelop
   3. reset
   4. replay
   5. unwise
E.

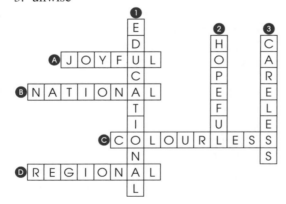

22 Rupinder the Reporter

A. Paragraph One: A
   Paragraph Two: A
   Paragraph Three: B
   Paragraph Four: B
   Paragraph Five: B

B.

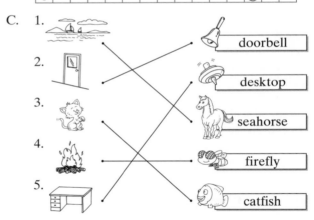

C. 1.
   2.
   3.
   4.
   5.

   doorbell
   desktop
   seahorse
   firefly
   catfish

D. (Individual drawing and word)

23 A Special Project

A. 1. wool and crochet hooks
   2. 24
   3. white wool
   4. a large rainbow-coloured blanket
   5. to an orphanage

ISBN: 978-1-897164-31-0

B. (Individual drawing)
C. 1. circle
2. very ; cloth
3. beside ; couch
4. dear ; loose
5. pass
6. It's
7. dessert
D. 1. quite
2. curb
3. pours
4. set
5. nine-storey
6. principal
7. bold
8. stripes
E. (Individual writing)

24 Durian

A. Fruit: cherries ; cranberries ; durians ; pears
Animal: wild pigs ; squirrels ; orangutans
Place: Malaysia ; Thailand ; Singapore ; Canada
B. 1. oval
2. 5
3. 40
4. 30
5. greenish-brown
6. yellowish
C. 1. large ; small ; huge
2. hate ; like ; dislike
3. speedy ; slow ; swift
4. yummy ; tasty ; flavourless
5. overcast ; sunny ; bright
6. pleasant ; warm ; stormy
7. boring ; absorbing ; amusing
D. (Suggested answers)
1. chilly
2. vacation
3. untidy
4. hot
5. permitted
6. leaves

E. (Suggested answers)
1. I often try exotic fruits.
2. This store closes on Sundays.
3. The young lady is choosing a big durian.

25 The Story of Honey

A. 1. largest
2. one
3. laying all the eggs for the colony
4. five years
5. helping the queen make eggs
6. up to eight weeks
7. Worker Bee
8. 60 000
9. collecting nectar from flowers to make honey
10. making the honeycomb from beeswax to store honey
11. about five to six weeks
B. 1. ✔   2. ✔
3. ✔   4.
5.   6. ✔
7.   8.
9. ✔
C. 1. a ball
2. snails
3. coffee
4. a stone
5. a hotel
6. birds
D. (Individual writing)

26 Hello around the World

A.

Africa — Ni hao
China — Namaste
Israel — Shalom
Thailand — Sawatdee
Canada — Hello
Germany — Guten tag
Japan — Ohayo
Hawaii — Aloha
Korea — Anyong haseyo
India — Namaste
Spain — Hola
Italy — Bongiorno

Ohayo
Aloha
Jambo
Bonjour
Ni hao
Hola
Hallo
Hello
Bongiorno
Anyong haseyo
Guten tag
Shalom
Namaste
Sawatdee

B. 1. but
    2. or
    3. but
    4. ✔
    5. but
    6. ✔
    7. and

C. 1. or
    2. but
    3. or
    4. and
    5. and
    6. but

D. 1. I wanted to call Tracy but her line was busy.
    2. I'll get some snacks and you'll prepare the drinks.
    3. Put your shoes in the box or leave them on the rug.

27 My Brother, the Babysitter

A. 1. B   2. B
    3. A   4. A

B. 1. He took special classes at a babysitter school last year.
    2. (Any one of these)
       Where are you going?
       When will you be back?
       What is your cellphone number?
       Where is the fire exit?
       What is the fire meeting point?
    3. (Individual answer)

C. 1. Does
    2. Do
    3. Is
    4. Were
    5. Are
    6. Did
    7. Was

D. (Individual writing)

28 Marsupials

A. 3 ; 1 ; 2 ; 4 ; 5

B. 1. Marsupial babies are born blind and hairless.
    2. The baby has to find its mother's pouch on its own.
    3. Most marsupials live in Australia.
    4. The opossum is about the size of a cat.

C. (Cross out these sentences.)
    Paragraph One:
    You cannot find other kinds of marsupials in Canada.
    Paragraph Two:
    Honeybees are hardworking insects.
    Paragraph Three:
    A spider is not an insect.

D. (Individual writing)

ISBN: 978-1-897164-31-0

Review 2

A.
1. have
2. is
3. call
4. is
5. is
6. does
7. come
8. are
9. have
10. smiles
11. reminds
12. is
13. laugh

B.
1. Pui Pui's body is covered with thick, white fur.
2. She has black eye patches, ears, legs, and shoulders.
3. She likes eating fresh bamboo leaves and shoots.
4. She eats fast to stay healthy.
5. She likes to walk slowly in the forest.
6. She can climb trees easily.

C.
1. walked
2. in
3. was
4. hoped
5. stood
6. under
7. on
8. heard
9. got
10. came
11. above
12. looked
13. saw
14. in
15. said
16. became

D.

E.
1. ice
2. cheetah
3. desert
4. seed
5. peach
6. sea
7. fly
8. swan

F.
1. quiet
2. dinner
3. dessert
4. very
5. past

G. (Suggested answers)
1. Do you like bamboo shoots?
2. What do you like to eat?
3. Why do you like bananas?
4. Are there bananas in this forest?
5. When do you eat bananas?
6. What else do you like eating?
7. Which do you like eating better, bananas or pears?

ISBN: 978-1-897164-31-0

1 Aboriginal Peoples

A. Iroquoians: Neutral
Wendat
Petun
Haudenosaunee
Algonquians: Nipissing
Abenaki
Ottawa / Ojibway
Ojibway / Ottawa
Algonquin

B. Petun: A
Neutral: B
Haudenosaunee: C
Ottawa: A
Algonquin: C
Abenaki: D
Nipissing: B

2 Houses of Aboriginal Peoples

A. 1. Iroquoians   2. longhouse
3. clan   4. village
5. beds   6. storage
7. family   8. Hearths
9. fires   10. warmth
11. storage   12. bed
13. hearth

B. 1. F   2. F
3. T   4. T
5. 2 ; 4 ; 1 ; 3

3 What Aboriginal Peoples Ate

A. 1. corn
2. squash
3. beans
4. squash

B. Hunting: A ; E
Trapping: B ; D
Fishing: C ; F

C. 1. beaver   2. rabbit
3. wolf   4. moose

4 What Aboriginal Peoples Wore

A.
For men:
For women:
For children:

B.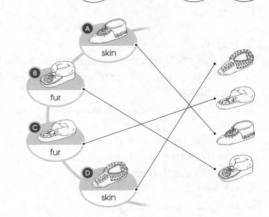
A skin
B fur
C fur
D skin

C. 1. thread   2. weaving
3. thread   4. needle
5. cloth   6. weaving

5 How Aboriginal Peoples Travelled

A.

B. 1. Ada   2. Tom
3. Ben

C.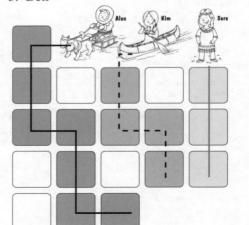

ISBN: 978-1-897164-31-0

6 How Aboriginal Peoples Used Corn

A. Cob: E ; H
   Husks: C ; F ; G ; I ; K ; L
   Kernels: A ; B ; D ; J

B.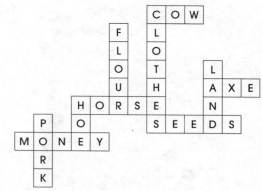

   maize
C. 2 ; 1 ; 3 ; 4

7 How Aboriginal Peoples Used Bark

A. 1. It's waterproof
   2. Because it's strong
   3. It's easy to twist
   4. Is easily found
B. 1 ; 3 ; 4 ; 5 ; 9 ; 12

8 Immigrants from Other Countries

A.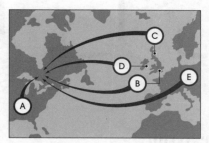

   Upper ; Ontario ; Europe ; immigrated
B. German: freedom of religion
   American: freedom of religion ; equal freedom
   British, Scottish, Irish: jobs ; land ; food

9 Journey of the Immigrants

A. (Individual drawing)
B. 1. A ; B ; D   2. A ; B ; D
   3. A ; C ; D   4. B ; C ; D

10 The New Land

A.

```
              C O W
        F     L
        L     O
        O     T         L
        U     H         A X E
    H O R S E           N
    P     O       S E E D S
M O N E Y
    R
    K
```

B. a. 5   b. 3
   c. 2   d. 4
   e. 1

11 Jobs of the Settlers

A.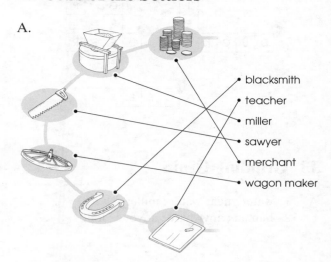

   blacksmith
   teacher
   miller
   sawyer
   merchant
   wagon maker

B. 1. plant / harvest ; harvest / plant ; butcher
   2. cook ; milk ; make ; plant
   3. feed ; wash

ISBN: 978-1-897164-31-0

12 Food of the Settlers

A. 1. corn
3. cabbage
5. beans
7. oats

2. wheat
4. peas
6. potatoes
8. pumpkins

Animals

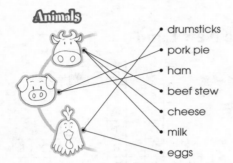

drumsticks
pork pie
ham
beef stew
cheese
milk
eggs

B.

13 Grinding Grain

A. 1. water ; near water ; miller ; short
2. human ; anywhere ; anyone ; long

B.

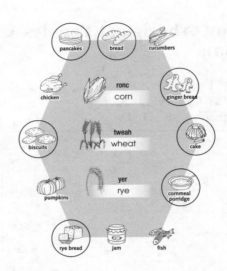

pancakes
bread
cucumbers
chicken
ronc — corn
ginger bread
biscuits
tweah — wheat
cake
pumpkins
yer — rye
cornmeal porridge
rye bread
jam
fish

14 Learning from Aboriginal Peoples

A. 1 ; 3 ; 6 ; 7 ; 8

B.
food
travel
medicine
leisure

The settlers learned how to grow corn.

Every part of the witch hazel plant had healing properties.

Canoes were one of the best ways to travel around Upper Canada.

The game of lacrosse was an important part of the Iroquoian culture.

Tea made from spruce tree twigs cured scurvy, the sailor's disease.

The settlers learned how to travel over snow using snowshoes.

The settlers learned how and where to trap animals.

C.
Start
Finish

15 Maple Syrup

A. 4 ; 3 ; 2 ; 1
3 ; 1 ; 2 ; 4

B. 1. sap
3. syrup
5. sweet
7. sugarbush

2. sugar
4. snow
6. spile

ISBN: 978-1-897164-31-0

16 Then and Now

A. 1. B   2. C
   3. A

B. 1. F   2. T
   3. T

C. (Individual answers)

17 The Compass Rose and the Scale

A. 1. northwest   2. northeast
   3. southwest   4. southeast

B. 1. north   2. west ; south
   3. northwest   4. southeast

C.

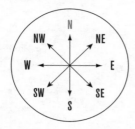

1. 5 km ; 50 km
2. northeast ; southwest
3. it shows distances between towns, not buildings

18 The Legend

A.

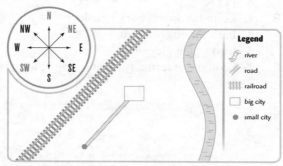

5. (Individual drawing of the new item)

B. 13 ; 1

19 More about Maps

A. 1. 40 km   2. cities
   3. south   4. Green Earth
   5. railway ; west

B. 1. landforms ; province ; lake
   2. territories ; location
   3. roads ; neighbourhood ; house

20 A Look at Canada

A. 1. Yukon   2. Nunavut
   3. Quebec   4. Alberta
   5. Saskatchewan 6. Ontario
   7. New Brunswick 8. Quebec
   9. Manitoba   10. east
   11. Pacific Ocean 12. north

B. 1. Northwest Territories
   2. Newfoundland and Labrador
   3. British Columbia
   4. Nova Scotia
   5. Manitoba

21 A Closer Look at Canada

A. 1. St. John's
  2. Charlottetown
  3. Yellowknife
  4. Victoria
  5. Fredericton
  6. Iqaluit
  7. Edmonton
  8. Whitehorse
  9. Toronto
  10. Québec City
  11. Winnipeg
  12. Halifax
  13. Regina

B. 1. Yukon
  2. Alberta
  3. Ontario
  4. Manitoba
  5. Saskatchewan
  6. Nunavut
  7. Quebec
  8. Northwest Territories
  9. British Columbia
  10. Nova Scotia
  11. New Brunswick
  12. Newfoundland and Labrador
  13. Prince Edward Island

22 Urban and Rural Communities

A. Urban: C ; G ; I
Rural: A ; B ; E ; F ; H
Both: D

B. 1. U
  2. R
  3. R
  4. R
  5. R
  6. U
  7. R
  8. U

23 Work and Play in Communities

A. 1. B ; D ; F
  2. A ; C ; E
B. 1. C ; rural
  2. B ; urban
  3. A ; rural
  4. D ; urban

24 Urban and Rural Transportation

A. 1. A. subway
   B. tractor
   C. taxi
   D. horse
   E. wagon
   F. double-decker
   G. logging truck
   H. streetcar
  2. Urban: A ; C ; F ; H
   Rural: B ; D ; E ; G

B. (Suggested drawing)

Urban Community

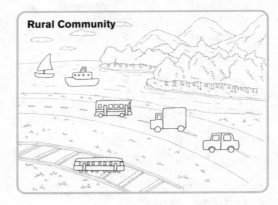

Rural Community

Review

A. 1. D
  2. I
  3. B
  4. G ; E
  5. H ; A
  6. F ; C

B. 1. kernels ; dress ; bark ; husks
  2. bark ; toboggan ; fur
  3. husks ; tea ; leggings

C. 1. Scotland ; Germany ; States ; land ; food ; jobs
  2.

  3.

  4.

ISBN: 978-1-897164-31-0

D. 1. blacksmith
   2. roots
   3. potatoes ; wheat
   4. maple
   5. bread ; porridge
   6. grist mill ; corn
   7. wagon maker
E. 1. Ontario
      Toronto
      trillium
   2. Quebec
      Québec City
      blue flag iris
   3. Yukon
      Whitehorse
      fireweed
   4. Nunavut
      Iqaluit
      purple saxifrage
F. 1. southwest ; northwest
   2. northeast ; west
   3. east
   4. road ; an urban

ISBN: 978-1-897164-31-0

1 Plants

A. 1. flower
    2. leaves
    3. stem
    4. roots

B.
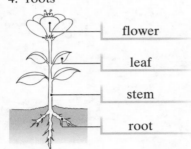
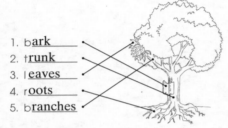

- flower
- leaf
- stem
- root

C.

1. bark
2. trunk
3. leaves
4. roots
5. branches

D. Broadleaf Tree: A, C, F
    Coniferous Tree: B, D, E

2 Leaves and Flowers

A.

A B C D

Fern: D
Maple: A
Grass: B
Oak: C

B. 1. grass
    2. fern
C. 1. pistil
       stamen
       petal
       ovary
       sepal
    2. ovary
    3. sepal

3 The Needs of Plants

A. 1. air
    2. water
    3. light
    Experiment (Individual observation)
    Light could not reach that part of the leaf.
B. 1. leaves ; thick
    2. float ; sunlight
    3. ground
    4. leaves
    alpine: C
    desert: A
    water: B
    woodland: D

4 Plants: Pollination

A. 1. moth
    2. butterfly
    3. bee
    4. wind
    5. hummingbird
B. Animal pollination: animals ; colours
    Examples: A, D
    Wind pollination: wind ; small
    Examples: B, C
C. 1. pollen
    2. stamen
    3. pistil
    4. seed
    5. scent
    6. nectar

ISBN: 978-1-897164-31-0

5 Seed Dispersion

A.

B.
1. 2 ; 1 ; 3 ; water
2. 2 ; 3 ; 1 ; wind
3. 1 ; 3 ; 2 ; animal

6 Plants: Life Cycles

A.

B. B ; C ; D ; A
C.
1. years ; months
2. leaves ; flowers
3. maple tree ; sunflower

D.

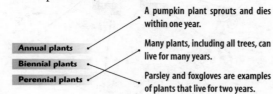

A pumpkin plant sprouts and dies within one year.

Annual plants

Many plants, including all trees, can live for many years.

Biennial plants

Parsley and foxgloves are examples of plants that live for two years.

Perennial plants

7 Uses of Plants

A.
1. hard ; E
2. strong ; G
3. sweet ; C
4. soft ; light ; A
5. flexible ; strong ; B
6. soft ; fine ; D
7. flexible ; F

B.
1. needles
2. bark
3. trunk
4. sap

C. seed

8 Endangered Plants or Invasive Plants

A. A, C, D, E, H, I, J, K
B. Endangered ; Invasive
C.
1. habitat
2. extinct
3. endangered
4. protected
5. invasive
6. native

9 Rainforests

A.
1. A ; Emergent
2. D ; Floor
3. E ; Floor
4. B ; Canopy
5. C ; Understorey

B.
1. animals / plants
2. plants / animals
3. canopy
4. seeds / fruits
5. fruits / seeds
6. Birds
7. layer
8. dense
9. rainfall
10. understorey

ISBN: 978-1-897164-31-0

11. forest floor
12. vines

10 Force as a Push or Pull

A. 1. Push
   2. Both Push and Pull
   3. Pull
   4. Push
   5. Pull
B. 1. gravity
   2. static electricity
   3. magnetism
C. 1. Direct Contact ; Push
   2. From a Distance ; Pull
   3. From a Distance ; Pull
   4. Direct Contact ; Push

11 Forces and Movement

A. 1.

2.

3.

4.

5.

6.

B. 1. 3 ; 1 ; 2
   2. 1 ; 3 ; 2
   3. 2 ; 1 ; 3
   Colour picture number 2 for 1-3.

12 Gravity

A. 1-3 and 5. Draw an arrow pointing down.
   4. No Gravity
B. 1. Jupiter ; Earth ; Venus ; Mars
   2. Mars
   3. Jupiter

13 Friction

A. 1. friction   2. friction
   3. FRICTION   4. FRICTION
B. 1. rough ; increase
   2. harder
   3. bicycle grease ; reduce
   4. slippers with rubber soles ; increase

14 Magnets

A.
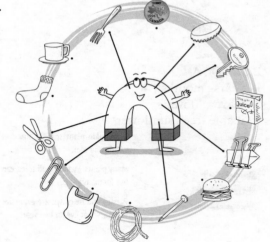

ISBN: 978-1-897164-31-0

B. 1. glass
    2. cloth
    3. wood
    4. plastic
C.

2.

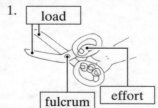

3.

15 Magnetic Poles

A. 1. south, north
    2. attracts
    3. repels
B.

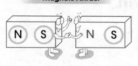

C. 1. attract
    2.

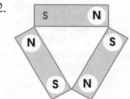

    3.

D. 1.

16 Stability

A. 1. B   2. A
    3. A   4. B
B. 1. thicker
    2. stronger
    3. beams

17 Levers

A. 1, 3, 4, 6, 7
B.

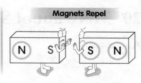

C. Part 1: easy ; little
    Part 2: harder ; greater
    Part 3: easier ; lesser

18 More about Levers

A. 1.

load

fulcrum   effort

ISBN: 978-1-897164-31-0

2.

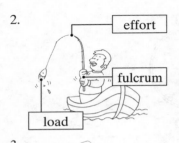

3.

4.

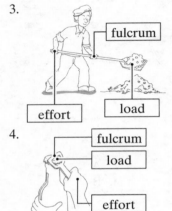

B. 1. lever
    2. easier
    3. easier
    4. greater

19 Soil

A.

B. A: waves
    B: rain
    C: plants
    D: wind
    E: river
    F: glacier

C.

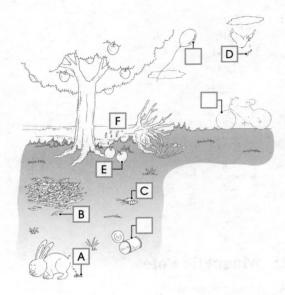

20 More about Soil

A. clay
    silt
    sand
    loam
B. 1. clay
    2. loam
    3. sand
    4. silt
C. 1. clay
    2. loam
    3. loam
    4. a. sand
       b. silt
       c. clay
       d. sand

21 Soil Erosion

A.

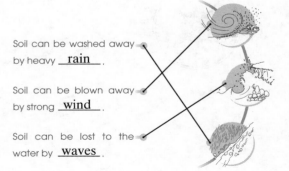

Soil can be washed away by heavy __rain__ .

Soil can be blown away by strong __wind__ .

Soil can be lost to the water by __waves__ .

ISBN: 978-1-897164-31-0

B. 1. B
    2. A
    3. C
    4. D
    Experiment (Individual observation)

22 Earthworms

A. 1. food
    2. castings
    3. predator
    4. tunnel
    5. habitat
B. 1. E
    2. D
    3. A
    4. B
    5. C
C.
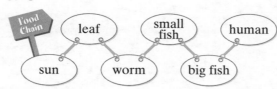

23 Creatures that Use Soil

A. 1. china
    2. skin mud mask
    3. soil field
    4. flower pot of soil
    5. peat fuel
    6. clay brick
B.
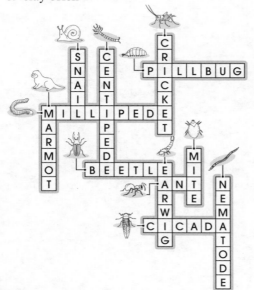

24 Compost

A. · Items from garden

· Items from kitchen

· Items from other places

B. 1. true   2. true
    3. false   4. true
    5. true
C. Composting is a wonderful way to recycle organic items.

Review

A. 1. light
       air
       water
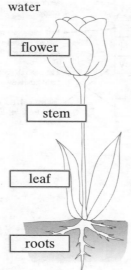

flower

stem

leaf

roots

ISBN: 978-1-897164-31-0

2.

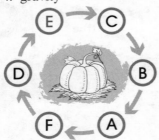

- pistil
- stamen
- petal
- ovary
- sepal

    3. stamen
    4. petal
    5. ovary

B. Animal Pollination: A, B, D, F
    Wind Pollination: C, E

C. 1. animal
    2. water
    3. wind
    4. gravity

D.

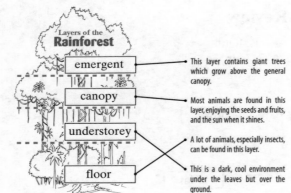

E.

Layers of the **Rainforest**

- emergent — This layer contains giant trees which grow above the general canopy.
- canopy — Most animals are found in this layer, enjoying the seeds and fruits, and the sun when it shines.
- understorey — A lot of animals, especially insects, can be found in this layer.
- floor — This is a dark, cool environment under the leaves but over the ground.

F. 1. Push ; small
    2. Pull ; great

G. 1. south
    2. north
    3. attracts
    4. Different
    5. repels
    6. Same

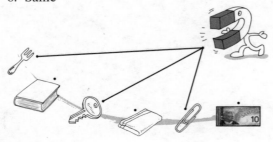

H. A, E, F

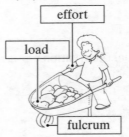

effort
load
fulcrum

I. clay ; D
    silt ; C
    sand ; A
    loam ; B

J. 1. A, B, D
    2. A, B, C
    3. A, B, D, E
    4. A, B, D, E

ISBN: 978-1-897164-31-0